Double trouble....

living with mania and depression

a personal story and practical guide

with

Tuscany  and a Recovery Journey

by Pauline Rhodes

ƐM Fourems Publications

Published by Fourems Publications, Hertford UK

Double Trouble with Tuscany and beyond

First published 2021

ISBN 978-0-9529765-7-8

Double Trouble first published 2007

ISBN 978-0-9529765-6-1

Printed by Herts & Essex Printers Ltd, Hertford

The contents of this book are based solely on personal
experience. The author has no medical qualifications and
anyone requiring advice about manic depression or issues
surrounding it should seek help from a registered medical
practitioner. This book is intended to help the families of, and
those caring for, sufferers understand more about living with
this very complex illness.

The information given in this book was believed to be correct
at the time of writing, but the author, the publisher and their
agents cannot accept responsibility for any errors or
omissions or any direct or indirect consequences thereof,
however caused.

Dedication

These books are dedicated to all those suffering from mental illness, especially Bipolar Disorder, their families and friends.

Acknowledgements

I would like to thank everyone who has helped me throughout the 30 years of my illness especially those who have supported me on my Recovery Journey for the last 14 years.

I would like to record my thanks to the late Eric Scott who made publication possible and to Marian Rutland, Michael Scott and Melanie Elliot co-owners of Fourems Publications for their help, support and encouragement. Other key people are Mike Inns for the cover design; Barry Pywell for his proof reading skill and to my GPs Dr Jan Cembala, Dr Gerry McCabe and Dr David McLees for their outstanding medical support. Special thanks also go to Robin and Chris for letting me share some turbulent times in their lives in this book. Thanks must also go to Revd Richard Allen, Steve Wright and Sandra Hayes for forming such a valuable support network.

Finally no thanks would be complete without those of my "belt and braces" my long suffering husband Nigel and my twin daughters Jenny and Helen who have lived through the stories and surrounded me with love. I would also like to mention Tom Readman and David Carter and my whole family who have enriched my life.

Foreword by the Bishop of Hertford
Rt Rev Dr Michael Beasley

"God only knows!" Words we cry when we are
bewildered and anxious, out of our depth and
afraid, afflicted and facing forces beyond our
control. To make such a cry is not only to give voice
to frustration and pain. It is also to acknowledge a
truth. This is that so much that happens to us in life
is unknowable, outside our command, mysterious.
We ask "Why has this happened? "What caused
this? How can I can make sense of my
experience?" To cry "God only knows!" is to make a
statement of faith that *somewhere* there is a
rationale for the experience we have to bear. It's
also to accept that in this life, finding explanation for
our circumstances may never be attainable. If there
is a truth to be found, it is beyond our ken.
Wrestling with such mystery has been the work of
human beings down the millennia. The most
famous example is the Bible's Book of Job. In
"Double Trouble with Tuscany and Beyond",
Pauline Rhodes adds to our human endeavour
through her own accounts of what it is to contend
with the unknowable, the uncontrollable, the
unreasonable; her own experience of manic
depression.

If it's true to say "God only knows", a truth not far
behind is the limited extent to which any of us fully
knows ourselves; what drives us, motivates us,
leads us. There is so much we can't bear to

acknowledge or fear to open up. The power of Pauline's account lies in her willingness to lay before us the impact of the uncontrollable force of manic depression on a life remarkably similar in almost every other respect to our own or those of our friends and relations. Pauline's story is the everyday stuff of getting married and having children, of the death of parents and the sadness that brings, of going to work and going on holidays. But for Pauline, all of this is stalked by the continuing possibility that all this normality could be plunged into jeopardy almost at a moment's notice, either by entering the depths of depression or the beyond control experience of mania with its attendant risk of being sectioned. And the question this poses for the reader is "If this is what's true for Pauline, what's there to stop it being true for me?" To which it doesn't take long to arrive at the answer "Just good fortune I suppose."

What God does know and that we can know too through Pauline's account is the extraordinary strength of human spirit that can be present in anyone's life around us. The most disturbing aspects of Pauline's story are the sheer violence that has sometimes attended her illness and the ways in which this and other factors act to erode human dignity and value. Pauline no more chose or "deserved" her situation any more than a person can choose of "deserve" short-sightedness or the colour of their hair. Yet its impact has been to effect daily assaults on her spirit through stigma and discrimination, brutality and restraint, frustration and guilt, panic and fear; a cumulative toll that acts steadily to bull-doze all that gives a person a sense of their own value and worth, agency and ability. In the face of such destruction, Pauline's story speaks of amazing possibility. Of the value of hope and determination, of deliberately making and holding space to be a contributor and maker of achievements.

When I first met Pauline I was captivated by her being introduced to me as an 'expert by experience'. It's a fabulous term that her book more than justifies. Certainly for all the practical advice and wisdom it contains. But much more for immersing its readers into the raw reality of what mental illness means. God only may know the full significance of every part of Pauline's life but reading it, we know much more than we began with both about her life and our own. Part of this is Pauline's own response of faith in all that has happened to her. It's a faith that encompasses uncertainty and doubt, questions and unresolved possibilities. It has no place for glib answers or rigid conclusions. Yet it's a faith that helps and salves, builds up and nurtures. It knows that ultimately "God only knows" but within that there is dignity and worth, kindness and care – an expertise, an experience of the greatest value.

Double trouble....
living with mania and depression

a personal story and practical guide

First published in 2007

Contents

1. Some background to Manic Depression/Bipolar Affective Disorder

What do Stephen Fry, Winston Churchill, Spike Milligan, Frank Bruno and this author have in common? We have all suffered from Manic Depression.

I was surprised to discover so many famous people were sufferers, but I was equally surprised that around one in a hundred people in Britain are diagnosed as having manic depression (now called Bipolar Affective Disorder) – and with a population of almost 60 million that means there are about 600,000 people suffering from it, so it is more common than many people think.

It is a serious mental health problem but, like a number of others, it is one which affects sufferers in ways which mean they often deny they are ill. It causes extreme mood swings and affects people very differently. Some experience more manic episodes where they feel incredibly well, vibrant, generous, and full of energy which, in my experience, has resulted in being sectioned under the Mental Health Act and consigned to a psychiatric unit under sedation! Others will experience more depressive phases where they are at the bottom of a black pit with no escape. The isolation of this is terrifying and the sense of hopelessness and despair indescribable and unbearable and I have known several people who have committed suicide during one of these phases.

Manic Depression is not a disease which can be caught. It can strike anyone at any time. It is often triggered by bereavement or other major life stresses, such as redundancy or divorce, but it can be a culmination of mental health problems such as severe depression or overpowering anxiety. There is a theory that some people are born with a tendency towards it, but this does *not* mean it will necessarily run in families.

Mine began life as an illness called "manic puerperal psychosis" which literally means a manic illness developed within six weeks of giving birth. Having given birth to twins by emergency Caesarean, had some ovarian cysts removed, had my sacra ileac joint displaced, suffered a massive haematoma which dispersed through the skin of my stomach and suffered paralysis through post operative shock – I was not feeling at my best but little did I know that as soon as I started to feel full of energy and find myself awake most of the night making plans for our future, I was embarking on this strange illness. I was told when I was diagnosed that I was one in a million – because manic puerperal psychosis was such a rare illness. The Royal College of Psychiatrists now say " puerperal psychosis is rather rare and happens after only 1 in 500 births". So having spent two weeks in a maternity unit I was discharged only to be expected to be separated from my babies and sent to a psychiatric unit (which had a mother and baby unit that could only take one baby!) Naturally I refused and I was treated at home by my family doctor with much help and support from my family and friends. However when my twins were 13 months old I spent almost three months sectioned alone in the unit, which was hell. It has since been diagnosed as manic depression and more lately bipolar affective disorder but to me the name is immaterial. It seems most forms of mental illness have many facets in common. The important part has been learning to cope with the illness.

A doctor once explained to me that my mind was "playing tricks on me" and whilst during a manic attack this seems unbelievable, it seems equally unlikely when you are in the depths of despair! Having said that, it is true your own mind is deluding you. The other problem is that this, in itself, undermines your confidence, you don't know what to believe and can find yourself constantly searching for "normality".

I have likened my illness, which began 16 years ago, to being stuck in a lift with no control over where the doors will open. Even now I live in fear that the lift will start moving and stop either on the top floor or in the basement and I will find myself being sectioned once more.

Many people suffer far more extreme episodes than I. Some live in a semi-permanent state of hyper-activity and mania while others spend years in depression. I am lucky because my illness responds to medication and is generally controlled by daily doses of Lithium Carbonate but despite this I have been sectioned four times and spent months in psychiatric units. Because of this my bouts of illness have been interspersed with long periods of "normality" and I believe this is also quite common.

In order to help control my mood swings I have become tee-total because alcohol induces both mania and depression and I dare not risk destabilising my fragile mental state. This was quite hard when I began, but it does make me popular as a "taxi driver" and it is quite enjoyable watching other people getting drunk and suffering from hangovers!

There are many different treatments available many of which are long term. Because of my use of Lithium Carbonate, I have regular blood tests and I have to be very careful of other drugs having an interaction. Over the years I have tried counselling, complementary therapies and herbal remedies as well as exercise, anti-psychotic drugs and sleeping tablets. I have found listening to music, silk painting and writing therapeutic but even now when I am awake at 2 or 3 o'clock in the morning I can have flashbacks to the nightmares I have experienced.

Having said all that, in some ways the illness has enriched my life. It has given me a fascinating insight into the power of the human mind. It has enabled me to empathise with others suffering from severe mental illness and to offer them some comfort and hope and it has given my life a new dimension. Never again will I take good health for granted.

A word of caution about "Lithium": If you are prescribed either **Lithium Carbonate** or **Lithium Citrate** to treat manic depression, make sure you do not mix the two. Due to unforeseen circumstances, I did, and suffered some unpleasant side effects!

2. Respectable, efficient, successful career woman

Me, in 1980 before the illness. Photography courtesy of Kingsley Michael

Up until I gave birth I was pursuing a career in editing and public relations and my CV cited my key skills as an efficient administrator/organiser/co-ordinator; effective communicator at all levels; logical and creative thinking, while the personal qualities it listed were being well organised; self motivated; conscientious and having a sense of humour. I mention this because although it

5

was, and is, true to a certain extent, I have been told that when I am in a manic phase I am almost like a caricature of my self – my strengths and weaknesses are all amplified. When I am manic it is almost like looking at a sequin through a kaleidoscope. Everything looks very different, it is vivid, colourful and vibrant and you can see dimensions to it you have never seen before.

Certainly, when I am in a manic phase, I am aware of a desperate need to get my life back in order whether that be through tidying, filing or making lists. I know that I try to use my excess energy to restore order around me. To others it simply appears I am causing chaos. I certainly cannot perceive the reality that the chaos is in my brain and no amount of tidying will get rid of it! Like most women, I also enjoy shopping and when I am manic I tend to go on spending sprees buying presents for people because I know my illness is upsetting them. I know irrational shopping sprees are often a tangible facet of mania.

It has been suggested that living and working as I did, for over 10 years, to strict deadlines has meant that my life already had manic and depressive tendencies in it. I certainly know I lived on plenty of adrenalin to meet all the deadlines and found myself on something of "a high" when I met them and then tended to dip into negativity until I faced the next challenge but I really don't believe that this contributed to the onset of the illness. I had never intended to return to work full time after the birth of my twins, but I always thought I would keep my professional life ticking over with some freelance work.

Having said that, realising that it would not be sensible to resume my previous career was a great blow and I did feel a very real sense of loss. I did do some freelance work when the twins were about two, in an effort to drag myself out of depression, but I found the combination of deadlines, toddlers and illness didn't work – even when we employed help with childcare. Interestingly, just three years ago, in 2003, I was commissioned to write a series of articles for a local magazine which were published, but I found the world I returned to very different from the one I left in October 1989. Technology had moved on and I had to submit my articles on CD-ROM. I was also required to supply my own photographs, which needed to be taken on a digital camera – all of which I managed, but was a far cry from the typewriter and carbon paper I had to use when I was training!

I remember reading my CV many years ago and wondering what happened to the person I was. I also found it very strange to realise that very few people that I know now actually knew what I was like then. Certainly my daughters have never known me working full-time to deadlines and going to press conferences and public relations launches, but when I look back now I feel that those days were enjoyable but false. In that world most people were "plastic", everyone said "Hi, how are you?" and everyone replied "Hi, I'm fine!" No one really knew the people beneath the professional façade and I find meeting and getting to know real people much more rewarding.

I have also found that over the years many of the qualities I listed on my CV are still there but I am using them in a different way. The one which I completely lose during my illness is my sense of humour and I often feel this is the one I would benefit from most whether I am manic or depressed! In fact, I have a lifelong friend who says I'm never mentally ill I just suffer from a massive sense of humour failure. She has suggested "a raunchy novel and a stay in a health farm" would be the best medicine for me and I often think she has a good point!

The onset of manic depression certainly gave me many feelings of guilt and worthlessness and when you are deprived of your freedom (through being sectioned) and find yourself dumped in a psychiatric unit with just the clothes you are wearing, it is hard not to feel a helpless victim with no self esteem and no self confidence. Having to borrow money from a complete stranger to make a phone call home to request some clean underwear is degrading and demoralising and is certainly something that I never expected to have to do. I am sure there must be a better way of treating people with mental illness.

From my voluntary work at my local hospice I see the dignity accorded to people with cancer and I often feel that none of us chooses to have one illness rather than another, so why should people suffering from mental illness be subjected to such stigma, fear and degradation while those with cancer receive the very best? (Having said that, I don't, for one moment, feel that the cancer patients don't deserve their treatment, only that the disparity seems so unfair on others).

I have often felt that my illness might just as well be called "schizophrenia" because when I am very ill, I feel that I am a far cry from the respectable, efficient, successful career woman I once was, and I find it hard to relate to that person when I am locked up with an eclectic mix of people suffering from alcohol and drug dependency as well as many other forms of mental illness. I once found myself sectioned alongside a man who held a senior post in the local Primary Care Trust. He had suffered the death of a newborn baby and it had triggered manic depression and we spent quite a long time discussing the problems we faced in the mental health unit. I have often wondered if he returned to work and if so if his experience has made any impact on the way patients are treated!

One of the many things I have found about being in a mental health unit is there is a sense of camaraderie. It is a great leveller: most patients are keen to help in any way they can, be it by lending someone money for a much-needed phone call or just by listening to problems, and actually I have learned that this mirrors life. If you have a problem and you ask people for help, most will not refuse.

3. Motherhood and the birth of "Double Trouble"

Almost ten years before the birth of my twins I had been told that I would "almost certainly not be able to have children without medical intervention" so you can imagine my delight when I became pregnant without entering a scientific circus involving IVF or any other medical procedure. This joy was more than doubled when I discovered at 12 weeks that I was carrying twins. I don't know why but I had always wanted two children – I had never thought about having an only child which in the event was just as well!

My pregnancy went very smoothly and I carried on working until October when I could no longer fit behind the wheel of my car! I joined the East Herts Twins Club and made a number of good friends and even managed to keep swimming until December 15! Maybe things were just going too well! On Friday 15 I had a check up and concern was expressed about the smaller twin. I was admitted for monitoring on the afternoon of December 17 and, having just had my tea, all hell broke lose!

The following are extracts from a diary I kept at the time.

Sunday December 17 1989

The registrar was adamant: "I want them out now!" Something was wrong, radically wrong, only one twin's heartbeat could be found. All hell broke lose. My husband was banished and I was being "attacked". Nurses were everywhere. Needles were going in my arm, blood seemed to be spewing everywhere…the drip failed to go in properly. I was manhandled into an operating gown, given a revolting anti-emetic to drink and asked to sign a consent form. I was shaking from head to foot. The nurses ran down the corridor with the bed and we went to the theatre in a lift...the anaesthetist seemed to be strangling me as he explained "it is necessary to pinch the cartilage in your wind pipe to stop you choking on any vomit because you've only just eaten, it won't actually hurt but I believe it is an unpleasant sensation"...

What an understatement. I thought I had been choked to death and even now I hate anyone touching my throat. Each time I have experienced a manic episode since, one of my delusions is that I am being choked. So a huge crisis, a big drama, then at 9.43 and 9.45pm two tiny, perfect, beautiful baby girls. They were three weeks premature and both quite poorly. They had to stay in special care, two floors below me, for five days but I was nursed intensively for two weeks before I was allowed home.

Tuesday December 19 1989

As I lay paralysed, unable to move a single limb, my mind began to move at speed – I would never be able to look after my twin daughters, my life was at an end, would my babies survive? I must get help.

I was in a side ward on my own. I shouted. No one could hear. Was my voice paralysed too? No, of course not, I could hear myself speak, shout; someone must hear. I lay motionless looking at the emergency cord...it was 2 o'clock in the morning, surely I would be found soon...

"It is post-operative shock" the doctor said reassuringly. I will just lift your head and sensation will return" and so it did. The relief was incredible. When I lay down, sleep eluded me.

I now believe this was almost certainly the onset of my "double trouble" or manic illness. This is partially because of the vivid and intense recollection I have of this period in my life. In my experience each of my manic episodes has been very vivid and etched indelibly on my mind. I was once told by a health professional that "you won't remember any of this when you are better", but that is blatantly not true in my case.

There were some lighter moments. Father Christmas came to me, three times, as well as Jenny and Helen in special care. He brought them some little pink teddies and some clothes knitted especially for premature babies. When he came to me on Christmas morning I was in a very undignified state, having my abdomen examined by a doctor. What he saw gave him such a shock that his beard dropped off on the bed! The doctor passed it back to him, grinning all over his face and said "You might be needing this!"

Father Christmas, (student nurse Adrian Sweeney) whose beard fell off onto my bed!

Just after Christmas I suffered a massive haematoma from my abdomen, which is a haemorrhage through the skin. This happened while I was in the shower and I swung from the emergency cord like a bellringer! Nurses came rushing from all directions and carried me back to bed. It was actually a very serious, potentially life threatening event, but while a screen was erected over my chest, a nurse talked calmly to me and asked if she could get me anything. Much to her surprise, I requested a towel and a hairdryer! I have always hated dripping hair, so she set about drying my hair. It cannot be everyone who, when bleeding profusely, decides they want a blow dry! Years later I was told that this massive loss of blood could actually have triggered my manic depression but I will never know if it did.

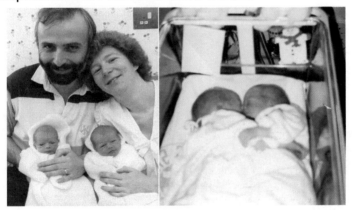

Above left: Right at the start of my illness: the first portrait of my new family on 26 December 1989. Photograph courtesy of Dick Smith.

Right: The first I remember of Jenny and Helen snuggled up together in a special care cot looking just as if they are kissing.

From then onwards life was a blur. I could not/dare not rest. I had two precious daughters to look after but I was too ill to be with them so I lay awake planning ahead. I wrote thank you letters and birth announcements…I made lists…I kept a diary…I did everything I could think of to take my mind off the sense of loss. The other new mothers had their babies. I had limited access to mine: all I had was a table over my bed, a pen and paper!

I remember the first time I saw them snuggled up together in a cot, they looked so tiny and fragile but just as if they were kissing! Suddenly I noticed they had names: Jennifer Mary and Helen Margaret – apparently, much to my husband's surprise, I had named them while I was still under the effects of the anaesthetic!

Having said that, having my beautiful, tiny, fragile daughters gave me a reason to live and was a major factor when, several months later, I was contemplating ending it all.

Although I didn't realise it then, by providing myself with an external focus (my babies) I focussed more positively on myself. (Finding an external focus has been something I have done a great deal since to help me through my most difficult times). I knew then that I could not let them grow up without a mother – even if I was going to be the worst mother in the world. Eventually I made myself believe that I now had "a belt" in my husband and "braces" in my daughters and they would keep me afloat through all the very difficult times which lay ahead.

I found it very hard when I did come home to let other people help me to look after them, but I knew I was still too ill to do it alone. One bonus was that my husband, my parents and my mother-in-law forged a very strong bond with them early on and they have always been very close to their dad and their grandparents. However, after my hospitalisation, when they were 13 months old, it became obvious that our family could no longer cope alone and we employed a qualified nanny who came daily and who was a great friend and support to me as well as the girls.

Leaving hospital on 30 December 1989, eleven days after what I believe was the onset of my "double trouble".

It was the last thing I had ever wanted to do to employ someone to look after my children and it was very hard to find the right person, but we were very lucky and almost 16 years later we still keep in touch with her. However, at the time, I felt that that decision was almost quitting motherhood and it made a very big impact on me and my self-confidence.

I have often been asked about the difficulties surrounding their birth and whether I had ever considered suing the hospital. My attitude is that mistakes were made, but because they became fine, healthy children, my own suffering has been tolerable. Had they not both survived, or had one of them suffered brain damage then the story might be very different!

4. Rock bottom – life in a psychiatric unit

Life was a rollercoaster from December to June when the girls were Christened. Because of the drugs I was taking I had to give up breastfeeding (which was about the only bit of motherhood left to me) and this caused me great distress. The girls took to bottles and dummies readily and I had always hated dummies so I felt that I was the biggest failure in the world. Our next door neighbour, a wonderful elderly lady suffering from cancer, who had lived to see our twins, died at the end of January and my back deteriorated badly in March.

Through most of 1990 I hovered precariously on the brink of depression. December was a terrible month. The girls and I all had chest infections and diarrhoea. "My little one" developed an ear infection on the eve of her first birthday and screamed all night. I greeted their birthday with a mixture of horror and delight and the Christmas which followed was actually worse for me than the one I had spent in hospital after their birth!

I spent four days of hell in January 1991 in a psychiatric unit, sectioned. I can recall little about this except that in my desperation I banged my head on the floor and broke my glasses!

Jenny (left) and Helen around the time I was sectioned for the first time. Being away from them, when they were so adorable, contributed to my "hell".

Another clear recollection which shows how strangely my mind was working is that I recall all the toilet roll holders on the ward had the name "Scott" on them! This may seem insignificant to you, as a reader, but to me at the time it was strangely significant. Eric Scott, was the editor who trained me to become an editor and who is still (aged 86) a very good friend.

Before I was hospitalised, I had been trying to contact him and when I couldn't, I assumed he had died and I started to write his obituary as follows:

"Eric Vernon Scott, one of a long line of Great Scotts has finally given up the ghost! His journalistic career led him to be the founder executive and news editor of the Deccan Herald and founder of Egon Publishers…a staunch Roman Catholic, Eric faithfully edited "Contact" on behalf of the Roman Catholic community in Britain…" At his point I decided I could not carry on and abandoned it, just as well really! I hope this illustrates how bizarrely the human mind works when it is manic.

My experiences have given me an innate fear of hospitals, doctors and drugs. In 2003 I had to go into hospital for an operation and I was absolutely terrified. I had to take sedatives so that I could be admitted and in 2004 I had to have a gastroscopy, where a camera is passed through your mouth and into the stomach, and I had to take sedatives before that too! My idea of hell on earth is being locked up in a psychiatric unit with no pen, no paper, no computer and no urge to function.

I hated everything about the unit. I hated the fact I was locked away from all I was living for; I hated the constant TV (especially the Gulf War) which seemed to be symbolic of the way I was being bombarded and held hostage. I hated being made to use the lifts when I was claustrophobic. I hated the food and the company. I hated the boredom and the lack of fresh air and exercise and I hated the staff who seemed to behave like power-mad prison warders rather than compassionate human beings. Some were kind and sympathetic but I felt victimised and oppressed. Human rights? It seemed to me psychiatric patients had none! Dignity and tender loving care were certainly not in evidence.

In fact, when I am in a psychiatric unit I do not even have the will to survive. About all I am left with is a strong spiritual conviction that somewhere in all this there must be a purpose. Perhaps it is that, through my suffering, and my ability to communicate, I can help others and I hope that by writing this I can do just that.

Although I had been discharged from the section, I was not discharged from the psychiatric unit until March 18 which, to date, has been my longest stay. The fact that I came out at all means that something must have improved while I was in there but I have no idea what! Being discharged gave me a little hope and I remember thinking I can live in hope and with hope and determination all things are possible.

When I left the unit I wrote the following:

"The lift door shut and that was that. I was terrified. I've always hated lifts. This was it, a vacuum to end all vacuums. Part of me knew I would never escape and now, eighteen months later, part of me is still struggling desperately to be free.

I know beyond the doors there is happiness. I know beyond the doors there is life others enjoy. My beautiful twin daughters, now eighteen months old, my loving husband, my home, my friends, my family – but I am a prisoner held hostage in a lift. The doors are transparent, I can see the joys of life but I cannot take part. Sometimes the cruel devil which holds the keys to the lift presses the button and I go down. Then I panic: I can see blackness, illness, horror and worst of all I am alone. No one can reach me down there, try as they might. Yet gradually, as I endure the darkness, imperceptibly, it lightens again and I rise to my old level.

Just occasionally the lift goes up and I am full of energy and fun and have an incredible zest for life but then the lift operator opens the doors and I find myself in hospital being sedated. It seems there is no ground floor where the door can open, just a basement or the top floor.

I face an uncertain future. We now employ a nanny to look after our children. I was a journalist and editor and now I have to face the fact that I may never work again. I do nothing most of the time except sit in the lift waiting for the doors to open. I take tablets daily and I cry a lot. I weep for what I have lost; I weep for what I am missing with my children; and I weep for the future I cannot face.

I have to come to terms with mental illness – "It takes time", the doctors say, "it is something you will come through" but when and how they cannot say. They expect a low after a high. I used to take level for granted, now I question everything. In the lift nothing is certain; I have no control, all I have is staying power and some days that seems to be at a very low ebb!

In Ray Moore's book 'Tomorrow is too Late' he cites a Tennessee Williams play in which he talks about someone plagued by bouts of depression and he apparently uses the imagery of a 'blue devil' perched on their shoulder constantly taunting them with sadness and sorrow. That 'blue devil' is operating my lift. Tennessee Williams said the only way out is to endure it because if you do, sooner or later the devil will tire and go away. He may come back but all you have to do is quietly endure it an hour at a time, a minute at a time.

And that is what I try to do but when my powers of endurance weaken I've taken to writing to try and scare the devil that way. To show him there is something in my life I can still control and to try to show others that *they are not alone with their illness, I am with them and so I am afraid are many others but we only have 'one devil' between us – DEPRESSION.*

There are people I have met who have conquered depression but it seems it has taken years and that, in itself, seems depressing. They say you emerge from it a stronger, better person – this is encouraging but at the moment it seems to me almost beyond hope that I will ever emerge again."

I know many people have written very powerfully about their illnesses and much of it is worth reading. I just wanted to include this because it shows exactly how my mind was working and I hope that other sufferers or their families might identify with some of it.

Fifteen years later... I am out. I hope to stay out. I try and manage my illness with a combination of drugs, common sense, diet, exercise and an increased awareness of my own need to relax and to be stimulated. I have regular blood tests and monthly check-ups with my GP and I do voluntary work two days a week.

As for when I emerged, I can't really say. It was very gradual and it took enormous tenacity. I am not known for giving in easily and I have always hated being beaten, which I guess is why I am where I am now!

5. Struggling to stay afloat – "you don't look like a psychiatric patient"!

Between 1990 and 1994 I struggled to stay afloat. I tried to look after my daughters and I loved watching them grow into little people with personalities. I tried to look after myself but I remember thinking that nothing was easy. One thing I did learn was that people are always willing to help. If I needed a lift somewhere or I needed someone to take my daughters somewhere help was always at hand, I only had to ask (that was a difficult lesson to learn!).

I learned too that illness is a great leveller. I had a very good friend who, at that time, had just been diagnosed with breast cancer. There were things she could do and things I could do and we helped each other. Our illnesses were vastly different but our needs (she had a four year old and a two year old) were often similar. Between us we had lots of friends who pitched in and helped and being able to share our ups and downs was really helpful to me.

I remember feeling deeply uncertain. If I felt good I was worried I was going manic, if I felt down I feared depression, but I took comfort from the people who, when told about my illness, said, "you don't look like a psychiatric patient!"

A rare picture of my husband and me. (I hate being photographed!) Do I look like a psychiatric patient? Photograph by Peter Ruffles.

I asked myself then, and I have often asked myself since, what a "psychiatric patient" looks like. Someone helpfully told me that psychiatric patients wear slippers out of doors (well, I do that quite a bit!) but in my experience people suffering from mental illness come from all walks of life. I have met members of the clergy, doctors, academics, tv repair men, dinner ladies and numerous others whose background I haven't even known.

My point is that mental illness, like any other illness, can afflict anyone and although there may be "tell tale signs" which largely happen as side effects to the drugs (such as rocking back and forwards or shaking uncontrollably) there is no such thing as looking like a "psychiatric patient".

"Psychiatric patients" are people with an illness which happens to affect them mentally. They are often more scared of themselves than likely to harm anyone. The nature of mental illness is such that it cannot easily be understood by the sufferer or others and the media seem to delight in labelling people "a danger to the public" when they are mentally ill. This leads to a

24

disproportionate fear of people with mental illness and tends to make them feel even more isolated. I am certain statistics show that more people are killed or injured by cars on the road, drunks on a Friday night and people taking illegal drugs than by people suffering from severe mental illness but human nature and the media seem to be happier to accept the first three groups rather than the last.

Looking back I think this was a period when I tried to come to terms with living with my illness, living with this "psychiatric patient label", and began to learn to "hold my head above the water" and get on with life. I came off lithium carbonate on the advice of my GP and I *seemed* to be relatively stable. I know I did a lot of reflecting on what might have been and I dabbled in some freelance work. My father was ill and was facing major heart surgery; my husband was due to go to France on a business trip and then the IRA exploded a bomb at the end of my parents' road on the railway line in Old Stevenage. It might have been exploded in my head because on August 2 (my niece's 5th birthday) I was re-admitted to the psychiatric unit.

On this occasion I walked miles round Old Stevenage and went on a shopping spree, buying presents for everyone, because I had such a sense of failure and guilt. I now know that wild shopping sprees are often part of manic illness. Stephen Fry recently admitted that during a manic episode when he was 17 "I bought ridiculous suits with stiff collars and silk ties from the 1920s, and would go to the Savoy and Ritz and drink cocktails".

I was deluded and manic again. I was bitterly disappointed and I was back to square one…I felt helpless, hopeless and furious when I realised I was going to be sectioned again. I felt a burden to my family. I was a further worry to my parents; my husband missed his trip to France and I felt my world had collapsed.

In desperation, I grabbed a fire extinguisher from the wall at the entrance to the unit and let it off at the policemen who were trying to get me admitted. (This is the only "dangerous" thing I have ever done during my illness and I feel ashamed to mention it, but I think it is important because I felt so trapped and desperate.) Sending police officers and paramedics along with social workers and other members of the "crash team" seems to be a disproportionate response to a middle-aged woman who has lost the plot and is "throwing a wobbly" because she can't handle the stress of life. Calm, gentle persuasion and perhaps a little tea and sympathy (with maybe a Mars bar) would certainly make me feel more ready to co-operate and go to hospital!

When you are confused, scared and desperate being confronted by "the cavalry" is enough to drive you insane! I have often wondered if, when I discharged the extinguisher, I looked like a "psychiatric patient" or just a desperate woman. I know which I felt!

6. The death of my father - another spell in hell

My father, very at home with a book, a pint of beer and a pipe! He contributed a unique blend of mild eccentricity, wonderful sense of humour, pragmatism and common sense to my life which has helped me come to terms with my illness. Photograph by Barry Pywell.

My father's death was sudden. He had been unwell with heart problems for more than ten years. He had survived major heart surgery in December 1994 but during 1995 he did not improve as he hoped he would. At the beginning of October his legs began to swell and he was taken into hospital and was waiting to be transferred to Harefield when he died.

Looking back to December 1994, when we thought he was going to die, during surgery, is really rather amusing. My husband and I took him to Harefield and he said he wanted a word with me. Naturally I thought this would be a somewhat sad moment but all he said was "I know if I don't survive you will look after your mum, but please make sure she buys a reliable car and a decent lawn mower!" So that was it. My father had given me his last wishes!

My father was a very pragmatic and slightly eccentric man. From very young I can remember him telling us that there were "only two certainties in life, death and the tax man and if you've paid your taxes you have nothing to fear in life"!

His operation was carried out on December 2 and we had been told it could take five days for him to come round properly, so when, on December 3, my sister received a call from Harefield, she feared the worst. However, the caller said "Your father is insisting on speaking to you" and to her amazement he came on the line to wish her a very happy birthday and a very happy day it was for us all! He had said he would ring her on her birthday but none of us believed he would. To which he replied "O ye of little faith!" Apparently when he came round from the anaesthetic, the first question he asked was what date it was, and then he started asking to ring my sister. At first the staff thought he was under the influence of the drugs but when he persisted they relented. He was always a man of his word.

By October 1995 it was clear he was frustrated by his lack of improvement and his deteriorating health was getting him down. He had lost much of his will to live but he was convinced there was nothing wrong with him that Professor Yacoub could not fix. Having said that I do recall him saying he felt that not only had he passed his "Best Before Date" but he feared he might be past his "Sell By Date" so it was a much less positive man who went into the Lister Hospital to wait for a bed in Harefield.

Once in hospital, his spirit was broken. Almost three weeks later he was a desperate man. I asked him what I could do for him and he said "get me out of here!" I protested but he said no, find a wheelchair, get me a pint of beer and a cigarette, and take me outside for some fresh air. This desperation struck a chord with me and so on Thursday 19 October, I did just that. He was a changed man.

Fresh air, a pint of beer and a cigarette, restored his spirit. We sat for almost an hour in the late sunshine chatting and watching the world go by…he was his old self. We talked about me buying a new car and I chose the model and the colour with his help…the next day my mother got a phone call to say he was critically ill. They might be able to save his life by amputating his legs but otherwise he would have to be put on life support. We knew he would not want the former so we opted for the latter but were told he was not expected to last the weekend. He died early in the morning of Sunday 22 October.

I was initially relieved. I was pleased he wasn't suffering and I was pleased that we had enjoyed such a lovely interlude in the fresh air. I knew too well how awful being stuck in hospital felt. I knew he had lost much of the quality of life he had enjoyed and I knew he would be happy to finally meet his maker. What I didn't know was how we would all cope without him.

My daughters (then aged 4) took his death in their stride. Jenny made a very long paper ladder so that he could climb up to heaven while Helen took comfort from the fact that there was still a Lancaster flying, so that Grandad could go to heaven in it! (He had worked on Lancaster's during WW2, as an engineer, and always said they were his first love, my mother his second!)

It was a difficult time but I seemed to be coping and then my mother was taken ill and rushed into hospital with a blocked bowel. She was less than 8 hours from death when they operated and suddenly I was back in the hell of the psychiatric unit...

I felt guilty for leaving my sister to look after my mother, albeit that she was still in hospital. Locked up without the rest of my family I missed my father even more, and then there was the realisation that this was likely to occur again and again at critical points in my life.

Despair was persistent. I lay on the floor and begged to die and then the staff gave me an injection and I felt giddy and sick.

I discussed suicide with another patient who eventually jumped under a train. Her death hit me hard. Life seemed very cruel indeed...but I knew I could not end it all. Two other women sectioned with me, also went on to commit suicide but I remained convinced that my life was not mine to end. My life belonged to my family, especially my daughters, and I knew I owed it to them to get better but how? I also felt a deep underlying conviction, based on my faith, that suicide was not an option for me even though death held tremendous appeal.

When I came out of hospital I was not allowed to drive and I also found the law had changed and DVLA and the insurance companies needed to know about any long term medication you were taking. This meant that I didn't end up buying the new car my father and I had discussed for another 14 months, but, when I did, I managed to get the exact model and colour we had discussed and I loved it.

Since then, I have found being discharged from hospital very difficult because, after being sectioned, I have not been allowed to drive and I have to renew my licence more frequently (currently every 2 years). Given that I usually feel very weak and exhausted when I come home and that my confidence and self-esteem are at rock bottom, I am not in a good position to do a lot of walking or to tackle public transport. The latter is something I intend to tackle while I am well so that it is less daunting when I am ill.

I always feel that being without my car is like a bereavement and a punishment as it leaves me feeling very isolated and helpless.

7. Paralysed by fear and frustration, prone to panic attacks

I have very little recollection of this traumatic time in 1995. I know people say that the human memory is selective and only recalls the good bits but this was a really dreadful time and I recall almost nothing. Unlike during my manic episodes, I was so frightened I didn't even keep a diary.

I do know that there was a race on between my mother and me as to who would get out of hospital first. I desperately wanted to visit her and she was equally determined to come and see me. In the event within 24 hours of my release, my sister and I were arranging for her to move into a nursing home temporarily. She was still very poorly but being discharged from hospital and we knew that we could not look after her. She spent one of the worst weeks of her life in the home, surrounded by senile dementia patients, before her brother and sister-in-law took her home with them for some tender loving care. They came and picked me up, because once again I could not drive, and we finally managed to spend some time together which was mutually beneficial.

My mother's close shave with death made me value her even more and gradually together we looked at ways to face the future. At Easter 1996 she went "back to work" volunteering at her local hospice shop and in October 1996, following the death of my friend, in August, with breast cancer, I joined the Hertfordshire Fundraising Office of Marie Curie Cancer Care as a volunteer one day a week handling local publicity and helping organise fundraising events.

My sister, my mother and me (left to right) on my mother's 70th birthday, just five months after my father died. My mother had just started volunteer work and was a great inspiration to me. Photograph

My mother often helped me – especially on "Daffodil Day" when we collected together all day and she would then count the money with my husband. The team we organised to do the street collections regularly raised around £1,000 a day in exchange for the synthetic daffodils we offered in return for a donation. We were a small part of a national day raising awareness of the Marie Curie nurses and much needed funds for their home nursing service.

The daffodil was chosen because it is an international symbol of hope and somehow it gave us hope too. She and I had a lot of fun thinking of ways to raise money and she helped me organise a local Barn Dance to celebrate the 50th anniversary of the Marie Curie Cancer Care charity. We made a good team and together we decided we had become "do-gooders", a breed my father would often mock! We spoke almost every day and together we got on with our lives, something that we knew my father was adamant we should do. By the way, she bought a new car three weeks before he went into hospital and a new lawnmower while he was in, so I pointed out that she had fulfilled his last wishes with time to spare!

When I read that back, it sounds easy, but believe me overcoming the feelings of fear and frustration and all the panic attacks was not as easy as it sounds. I also had the added fear of losing my mother which would haunt me for another nine years but I started swimming regularly again to try and get fit and lose some weight and while the exercise definitely helped me mentally it took enormous courage. Sometimes I would be half way through a length and begin to panic and fear I would drown. As a result of this, I found a pool where I could stay in my depth and I would stop and reassure myself that I was OK and carry on. With hindsight, this was not very sensible, I should have gone with someone or told the lifeguards, but I survived anyway.

I regained a lot of confidence from organising public relations events. I proved I could still produce "column inches" and raise the profile of an organisation whose nurses had cared for my friend. I knew she would be pleased that I was not sitting at home moping. We had discussed returning to work and while she was certain she never would, I **doubted** that I ever would but she urged me to try and by volunteering I had. I had found a niche for myself and I felt it would benefit others in her situation. Because of her young family, she chose to be nursed at home so that she could be with them and I knew that this was something she dearly wanted. (I also knew it was something I would have wanted too in her situation). So somehow life had a purpose beyond survival and it began to feel almost worth living again. When you talk to other volunteers, they often have a need to work but volunteering gives them a bit more flexibility and it is symbiotic. The more you give, the more satisfaction you receive.

Panic attacks affect many people, lots of whom do not have mental illness. They are very frightening and debilitating and I have to say I have never found any one solution to them. Sometimes deep "diaphragmatic breathing" helps. Sometimes Bach's Rescue Remedy can stave off an attack and sometimes positive thinking, inhaling lavender and listening to music works for me. Although I have had them during the day, most of mine have been at night, so I now keep all my remedies by my bed!

I rarely have really bad attacks these days. I have now begun to recognise when they are likely to happen. When I am very tired, very stressed and then usually when I try and relax and go to sleep. I used to have attacks which lasted all night where I would be shaking all the time and urinating frequently. I have vomited and suffered diarrhoea too but if I fear I am heading that way now I book a massage or, as a last resort, take 10mg of Temazepam before bed. I know people who have thought they were having a heart attack during a panic attack and certainly my heart pounds and races. However, a good night's sleep always makes me feel much better. If I have to take three consecutive doses of

Temazepam I ring my GP and discuss the problems with him.

8. Music and lyrics – comfort and escapism

Long before I was ill, my father used to joke about living with three women and say the trouble was we didn't ever "switch off and let the set cool down". This was usually in response to one of us complaining that he had dozed off in the chair while watching TV and/or reading the newspaper! He maintained the human brain was just like a TV set, it needed to be switched off and allowed to cool down several times a day but he reckoned that it was mainly only men who had perfected the technique. The longer I live the more I am sure he was right!

However since the onset of my illness, those words have often come back to haunt me, especially when I have been manic or depressed. How I would love to have control of a switch to just stop all those thoughts whirling around in my head. When I am manic it is exhausting and when I am depressed I am just swamped by their negativity. Recently, while I was on the Expert Patients Programme, for people suffering from long-term illness, I started practising positive thinking and positive self-talk. After the first two days I felt thoroughly depressed because I realised just how negative I had become! However, I persevered, and now I am more positive than I have been for a long time. Whether I could manage to do it when I am depressed I don't know, but I would certainly try.

When my illness began my husband had bought me the double cassette of the musical "Love Changes Everything". He bought it for me to listen to while I was in labour, but as I never went into labour I listened to it by way of escapism from my health problems and the hospital generally. When I shut my eyes I could visualise Michael Ball on stage in the show which I had seen when I was seven months pregnant. I took great comfort from the lyrics and I loved his voice and it evoked happy memories so I listened to it as much as I could and it almost became my "switch".

Since then I have regularly used music as a retreat. Once I have recovered from the horror of realising that I only have what I am standing up in when I arrive at hospital, I try and make sure I have got plenty of Michael Ball CDs and spare batteries for my personal CD player. It is interesting how important lyrics become when you are detached from reality. I have homed in on certain music, especially by Michael Ball, because of the sentiment and the emotions. I have since been to two more of his concerts and I can visualise his cheerful face and his impish laugh more readily. For some reason it seems to help. One of my favourite "comfort zones" is to lie in a hot bath, or just on my bed, and listen to music. I often joke that I am just going for a lie down with Michael Ball and I do not want to be disturbed. I am sure he would appreciate the joke!

In the last five years I have also begun silk painting which is a wonderfully mind-absorbing hobby and one which you can do while listening to music. I find that if I make silk painted cards there is the added bonus in that other people are really thrilled to receive them. I have also painted scarves and small pictures and I find that watching the paint spread across the silk calms and absorbs my mind in a very gentle and satisfying way. When I was working at a drop-in centre for people with

Me with one of my large hand-painted silk scarves. Photograph courtesy Peter Ruffles.

severe mental illness, I introduced silk painting and it was very popular. Not only did the members find it relaxing but they also took great satisfaction from their finished items.

Sadly, silk painting has not been available in any of the mental health units that I have stayed in, but, interestingly, it is available to the patients at the hospice where I work as a volunteer and it is a very popular occupation. Although it is a relatively expensive hobby, at the hospice we find the patients buy the finished items and we recoup most of the cost.

I have often thought that instead of being sectioned in a psychiatric unit, I would recover more quickly if I were sent to a health farm where I could get exercise, be pampered, be fed well and take part in relaxation classes as well as being able to swim, have a massage, lounge in a whirlpool or steam room and generally chill out! I have found that sitting in a steam room or a whirlpool also helps me "switch off".

Certainly it would be more pleasant, less intimidating and more relaxing than being locked in a unit where alarms constantly sound and I feel completely unable to relax even with my music. (In fact, I have been criticised by staff for "cutting myself off" from life on the unit by listening to music all the time!")

Perhaps this is a just a female dream, but it seems that if I were most men, a TV, a newspaper and a cup of tea (or even a pint of beer) might be all that was required to achieve that blissful state of escapism when the brain is "switched off" and "the set" has a chance to cool down.

9. Doctors, consultants and alternative therapists

Anyone living with a long term medical condition will know that visiting doctors and consultants becomes a way of life. It is therefore helpful if you can build a good relationship with at least some of them. Somebody likened these relationships to marriage, in that they will involve give and take on both sides. Although I have always managed to get on very well with almost all the GPs I have seen, I have found hospitals and consultants, and especially their teams, very frustrating and I know I am not alone in this.

With a condition such as manic depression, continuity is very valuable and although consultants don't change very frequently their housemen and registrars do. This means that there is very little chance of seeing the same person more than twice and consequently there is a feeling of taking two steps forward and three back on almost every visit. If the doctor has no real idea of what to expect when you are well, how can he judge your behaviour when you are ill?

I remember one house doctor saying to me "You are speaking a lot and very fast, do you think you might be slightly manic?" Now everyone who knows me, would tell you I tend to talk: a) a lot and b) quite fast all the time. So when confronted by a doctor who says "Can you tell me a bit about yourself?" and I know I have to précis about 10 years medical history into ten minutes, I know I will speak even faster! I have to say I felt sorry for him but even sorrier for myself!

I have now reached a stage, through medication and self-management, where I have regular (monthly) check-ups with my own GP and have been discharged from the consultant and his team, which is working very well for me.

I am very fortunate in that my own GP has an excellent philosophy – one I'm sure most doctors have when they start practising – that he would rather spend 5 minutes making sure I'm staying well, than half a day, or more, trying to find a hospital bed so that I can be sectioned in a mental health unit. He has been practising over 30 years and I guess he is one in a million, but I'm sure there are others who operate with the same helpful holistic approach. Although I would not say our relationship is in any way like a marriage, interestingly he is very similar in temperament to my husband and he has a very similar sense of humour to his, which helps me greatly. I have to say, without his input, I very much doubt whether I would be writing this book at all.

Having said that I have been very lucky with my GP; I have also found some excellent alternative therapists. Although my GP has suggested there is little evidence to show they will help, I have tried acupuncture, counselling, aromatherapy, reflexology, the Bowen Technique, Indian Head massage and massage for therapy and I know I have benefited from them all in some way or another. When my GP suggests I must be mad to spend money on such therapies I reply "Yes, and I've been certified to prove it!" At least he and I have established a rapport which allows my sense of humour and his sense of incredulity to flourish side by side!

Unfortunately no one has ever offered me an alternative therapy on the NHS but my family has borne all the cost, believing that health is more important than wealth.

It always seems odd to me that if there is, say, a sudden death in a school, a team of counsellors is sent in. In all my stays in mental health units the only therapy I have been offered is art therapy and then only one session. Given that two of my stays were the direct result of the death of a parent, why did nobody even mention bereavement counselling? Sadly the NHS does not seem to see the value of alternative therapy in mental health and, in my personal experience, it has been extremely beneficial.

My advice to anyone suffering from manic depression is not to give up. Keep taking the medication but try as many alternative therapies as you can. If something works stick with it. I know people who have found yoga very helpful and others who find meditation and Reiki helpful.

Personally I find prayer useful and I have taken great comfort from the healing services run, once a month, in my local Church of England church, where hands are placed on my head while the vicar offers a prayer asking for, among other things, "healing and light".

I cannot pretend I have felt a sudden dramatic improvement and often I have felt desperate for a miracle, but I have found it very comforting to be treated in this holistic way by someone who treats me as a person with an illness, rather than locking me up like a dangerous criminal. I have discovered that quite a number of sufferers from manic depression have a strong faith, and I will discuss the role of religion in more detail later.

I would also say that whether you have faith or none, it is important to build good relations with doctors, consultants, therapists and any professional, such as a priest, who can be called upon when you are desperate. I look on a number of close friends, with a variety of backgrounds, as valuable DIY tools. Everyone has problems and many will be there for you when you need them. I try and look on my GP more as a friend – I also know someone who is a trained counsellor and I know two retired priests – who will always listen. There is always someone – The Samaritans for instance - who will be there for you but you do have to ask and it is not always easy to recognise that you need help, let alone ask for it!

NB. I am very well aware that this book does not deal with the medical issues and ethical problems associated with treating manic depression which can be very difficult. Clearly they would need to come from a medical professional, such as my GP.

10. Pushing back the boundaries: assessing my achievements

I have talked about how volunteering helped me to move on in life. It gave me a purpose and a feeling of professional fulfilment. The latter was something I never expected to find again after the onset of my illness. I recently reviewed my CV and since the onset of my illness in 1989 I have added the following:

March 2005 -present	**Day Hospice Administrator** (2-days a week voluntary job share)
June 2005 -November 2005	**Community Support Worker with Rethink at the Connect 3 Friendship club** Charity for people with severe mental illness (one day a week)
July 2004 – January 2005	**Certificate in Interpersonal Skills for Volunteers (Distinction) University of Wales Lampeter** **Organiser of Hertford's second Christmas Tree Festival**
April 2003 – June 2004	**Isabel Hospice Volunteer** (one half day a week) **Freelance writing for Hertfordshire Life** (paid)
1999-2003	**S. Andrew's Church, Hertford Parish Administrator** (paid)
1996-2002	**Marrie Currie Cancer Care Hertfordshire Fundraising Office Voluntary Assistant** (one day a week) **Total involvement with the charity over six years helped raise over £30,000**

When you realise that only the freelance writing, the post of parish administrator and the work for Connect 3 were paid work it shows what you can achieve through volunteering. When I say that, I don't mean what you can achieve for the charity, but how you can rebuild your skills, confidence and self-esteem.

I remember answering the advert for volunteers for the Marie Curie Fundraising office with a mixture of hope and trepidation. It was almost a year since my father had died, and just over two months since I had lost my friend to cancer and I felt compelled to do something. My "interview" was very relaxed and the fundraiser, who, although retired, has remained a good friend, did not recoil in horror when I mentioned my illness. She was more interested in how she could best utilize my skills and this felt like a real breakthrough for me.

We agreed that I would go into the offices, one day a week, and do everything from filing and making tea to writing local press releases, and soon I found myself doing all kinds of things. I organized a Golf Day in conjunction with our local newspaper and a Barn Dance to celebrate the charity's 50th anniversary. I was back in the real world helping others and I began to look forward to my Thursdays!

Although I started a paid job, one day a week, as Parish Administrator, in 2003, I maintained some contact with Marie Curie and continued to organize collections for them on Daffodil Day until 2002. Once the original fundraiser retired and the office moved, I decided it was time for me to move on too.

Joining Isabel Hospice as a volunteer was an easier step although it involved an induction course and learning more new skills. I have worked on reception in the Day Hospice as well as in the Volunteers office, helping to co-ordinate their work, and currently I "job share" two days a week with the administrator at the Day Hospice. I produce correspondence, statistics and rotas as well as doing filing, photocopying and making phone calls and I feel very much appreciated and part of a team doing something very worthwhile.

Never, in my wildest dreams could I have thought, in 1990, when I was so ill physically and mentally that in 16 years my CV would read like that. I mean me, help raise over £30,000, when I was a gibbering wreck with no will to go on! I would have sworn I would never be useful again – let alone use my talents to such effect! But there you are, I did it and I am sure I will go on achieving things. It didn't all happen overnight. I have gradually pushed back the boundaries of my comfort zone.

Instead of staying in bed paralysed by the fear and frustration of my illness, I started making a point of getting washed and dressed before lunch. Then I started dressing smartly instead of slopping around in track suits and I started wearing make-up to go out – like I used to do for work. It was all little tiny steps. Some days I failed. Some days I went back to bed and cried, but in time getting up and dressed became the norm. As soon as someone said "I like your blouse" "that's a nice necklace" or "that dress looks good on you" I started to be able to hide my feelings behind my appearance. I wore a mask of coping and doing so enabled me to cope better with everyday chores.

This lesson in life was sparked when I was in my teens and I was very upset having split up from a boyfriend. My father said "Come on, stop crying, put on a face and we'll go out. If you can put on a face you can do anything." I was puzzled and asked him what he meant and he said "When I joined the RAF during the war I knew I had to be able to kill someone if necessary and I was terrified. So one day I put on my uniform and went out onto the Sussex Downs. I took my rifle and I shot a fox. I hated killing it but I had proved to myself that by putting on that uniform, I could kill." So, he said if you put on some smart clothes and some make-up you can create a mask of coping with your heartbreak. I did, and I've done it many times since.

The strategy had lain largely dormant for years but now the less I want to do something, the longer I take to get ready and ensure that the mask hides my fear.

For my father's funeral, which I was dreading, I bought a whole new outfit and went to the hairdressers to have my hair done. For my mother's funeral, where I actually did a long reading, the day after I left the mental health unit, I wore a new dress and I put on my mother's favourite perfume! If I feel that I look my best, I cope better and it helps me fly in the face of my illness. (I read recently that one of the tell-tale signs of people suffering from severe mental illness is often a loss of appearance and a lack of personal hygiene so I now hang on to mine like grim death!)

When I assess my achievements, which are not earth shattering, I make myself look back at where I started with this illness and where I end up each time I am hospitalized. I know then that I have achieved an enormous amount because each one has involved me pushing thousands of tiny barriers of fear and panic aside – including the fear of failure – I feel a great sense of pride. I am proudest of all that I chose not to lie in bed and give in to all my negativity. I know many people, especially my family and friends, have helped and encouraged me every step of the way, but it was I who **chose** not to become bed-ridden with fear and grief. I really do believe that the only person who can tackle this illness, particularly the depression, successfully is the sufferer.

You can choose to stay locked in the lift, in the basement, or you can start to look for ways to let others know you are stuck and want to get out. Others can try and get you out, but if you don't try really hard you will still be stuck. It will take more energy, physically and mentally, than you think you can muster, but my father was absolutely right:

YOU DO NOT KNOW WHAT YOU CAN DO UNTIL YOU REALLY TRY!

My father was also very fond of saying:

IF AT FIRST YOU DON'T SUCCEED, TRY, TRY AND TRY AGAIN!

And they are probably two of the best pieces of advice I can give anyone who is trying to live successfully with this illness.

11. The role of religion – a test of faith?

When I was researching manic depression on the internet I came across a personal story by James Wooldridge entitled "Living with Manic Depression" in which he says: "Prior to my admission to hospital I was a struggling Christian and at many times I felt my situation was a test of faith. There were times when I could have given up and if it meant the crisis in my mind would stop, I'd have gladly done so. However, giving up was anything but an easy option and anyway, amongst the times of desperation there were also glimpses of a world that was so beautiful and full of love that I often broke down and cried with joy." His story is well worth reading, but this particular extract struck a chord with me and my experiences.

Like James, before my illness began I was a Christian. I have always gone to church, sometimes more regularly than at others, but I had never had a "defining moment" when my faith had been confirmed or denied. I guess I saw my faith as part of me. My parents were both Christians, and my father and his family all had a very strong faith. Sometimes, I almost felt I had "inherited" an element of Christianity which was a privilege and I treasured my faith and it gave me comfort.

On Sunday 17 December 1989, the day my daughters were born, I attended Holy Communion and prayed a very simple, if naive, prayer: "God, if it be your will, let these babies be delivered safely". At that stage I only knew I was going into hospital to be monitored in the evening.

To my amazement 12 hours later they were here! Now, I don't, and never have, seen what happened during and after their birth as an answer to my prayers, but my illness has raised questions about my faith.

As a result of my illness I became friends with a lady in her late 80s (she died aged 97), who had also suffered from manic depression. She very much saw her illness as a test of faith and we discussed this issue a lot. Like me, when she had suffered depression she had felt detached from, and forsaken by, God, but when she was manic she described herself as "flying with God" and I could identify very closely with her experiences too.

In order to try and deal with her "test of faith" she spent about a year living in a convent in Canada. While it obviously didn't cure her illness, it certainly seemed to help her and by the end of her life she had a very strong faith. I took great comfort from her friendship and she regarded me as a "special" friend because we shared so much that we could not hope others would ever understand.

She once told me that when she was too distressed by her illness to do anything else, she recited the Lord's Prayer, over and over, in her head. In his article James Wooldridge refers to: "A massive war between good and evil was being fought between my ears and having been taught that 'The Good Book' was a source of inspiration for many, I turned to it often, sometimes pounding my head with my copy while praying fervently as if my very life depended on it".

In my desperation, I have recited parts of the Communion service and begged for Holy Communion at 3 o'clock in the morning, while locked in psychiatric unit. I am sure this will sound very odd to many but it seems that manic depression, along with other mental illnesses, often engenders strong religious conflict.

Going back to the issue of "flying with God" when I am manic everything seems to make perfect sense. Life is very vivid and exciting and I feel very much in tune with my faith and very close to God, but when I am then thrown into depression life seems very cruel and the depths of despair conjure up visions of hell – a deep black pit with no obvious means of escape and barely a shred of hope. It is a place where there is no sign of God and yet, oddly, even when I have been in that pit I have refused to contemplate suicide because, among other things, I have said that I believe that my life is not mine to take. It belongs to God.

The fact that I am still here to tell this tale bears testimony to my faith and I am grateful for that.

Thankfully, these two very extreme religious experiences are not a regular occurrence but having experienced them I am left with trying to come to terms with my faith the rest of the time. I recently heard a sermon about Pentecost and the vicar described a sense of comfort and safety at being hidden from sight, when as a young boy, he used to hide in a wardrobe. This was how I felt with my faith before my illness. My faith and I lived together, privately, in a comfort zone which was not greatly challenged, but which I felt no need to challenge. In the sermon he then went on to talk about the power of God going through locked doors.

This made me think that perhaps when I have been in the pit of depression, and I have felt trapped in the lift with no access to the controls, my faith has actually been locked in with me and it is the power of God which has sustained me. Certainly, I don't think I would have accepted that explanation at the time, but looking back, I remember complaining that I felt almost equally trapped by my faith, which would not let me take my own life.

I am now thinking my experience may have been like the "Footprints in the Sand". There were two sets of footprints and when times got tough, there was only one, the walker felt deserted and questioned God, but He simply said "I was there, I carried you".

Equally, when I am manic and everything seems possible, and I feel I have the power to go through locked doors, maybe I am actually experiencing the power of God. The rest of the time I retreat to the comfort of my faith and try not to question it too much.

I also take heart from the fact that whether you are ill or not, faith can't be proved!

12. Starting work again and more volunteering

Following the last chapter, perhaps it is no coincidence that when I returned to some paid work it was for the church! It was, however, not something I did easily. I agreed to take on the hitherto un-charted territory of parish administrator for a trial period of three months to help our erstwhile Rector out. He had known me since just before my daughters were born, and they were now twelve. So we were not exactly strangers but having said that, when you come to work very closely with someone, you get to know them very much better.

Revd Graham Edwards, Rector of Hertford, St Andrew, who employed me as Parish Administrator. Photograph by Peter Ruffles

He was very confident in my abilities, not least because he was not computer literate and I was, but there were many times when I would joke that the computer was the work of the devil designed to drive me to distraction! However, for all my mistakes and heartache with the computer, I gradually began to make the job of parish administrator happen!

I was utterly amazed that so many of my seemingly lost abilities returned. Behind the title of "Parish Administrator" I was no longer simply a manic depressive. I functioned in many ways as professionally as I had done before my illness and the job was very different. There were many times when people complimented me on my diplomacy or tact, my thoughtfulness or my kindness, and I began to realise that they were witnessing aspects of my character which had developed through my own experience of illness. I hope I was never hard-hearted and hurtful to people with health issues, but I realised I had become really interested in people, and their illnesses and problems. Although most of my work was working from home on a computer, I really enjoyed the small amount of work I got involved with especially with the elderly and infirm.

As I have said before, I have always thrived on organisation and although, it was only, in theory, one day a week, being parish administrator did me the power of good. I would slip into the role and my illness would recede. The Rector and I shared a very good sense of humour and the laughter was very healing. I realised that, although I still saw the funny side of things, I rarely laughed – well who does sit at home and laugh when they have a long term illness? I did the job for three and a half years in the end and for the next two years I worked in a voluntary capacity as PA to the Rector until his retirement. I decided to leave to work as a volunteer at my local hospice because I really wanted to explore the people part of my work more. I also felt it would not be good for me to leave when he retired as that would leave a large vacuum for the parish.

Through being parish administrator, not only did I gain a great deal of experience, but I gained the friendship of the Rector and his wife who have come to know me and my family very well. They have been wonderfully supportive of us through some very difficult times and I hope will always keep in touch.

But what does all this say about my illness? I honestly don't think I could have done the job as well before I was ill. I am sure that my illness has given me new dimensions which I was able to use in the role. I have to say I don't think I would even have considered taking a job working closely with a clergyman who was heading for retirement – I often joked "I must be mad to do this, but I have certificates to prove it!" However, I certainly don't regret it. It improved my self-confidence, raised my self-esteem, helped me rediscover my sense of humour and the ability to laugh and therefore helped me to move on from my illness and find other challenges!

13. Moving forward – creating new challenges

If you read my CV, since 1989, in chapter 10 you will see that I undertook all sorts of new challenges as a volunteer working for Marie Curie Cancer Care. I arranged a number of publicity stunts to start with and then moved on to a Golf Day (which took a year and was run in conjunction with our local newspaper). I also organised an anniversary Barn Dance with about 250 people. This was all done with the support and expertise of the fundraiser for Marie Curie Cancer Care in Hertfordshire. I will admit I lost a lot of sleep over all of them and there were times when I wished I'd never started, but looking back now I am glad I rose to those challenges and I really loved the feeling of satisfaction when they were over. They gave me "a natural high" as opposed to a "high" through my manic illness and my involvement with them helped raise over £30,000 in 6 years – this was a tangible achievement.

Prior to my illness I had never thought of myself as a high achiever. I knew I had a tendency towards being a perfectionist and obviously editing and PR required that in no small amount but I just accepted that what I did was very normal and did not really question what made me do it beyond enjoying the writing and finding much of it very interesting. I always felt that I was living in a very "plastic world" where every press reception I attended everyone was "fine" and everything "good" or "fantastic" but I did it.

Since my illness, I feel I have moved into a different, more real, world. My volunteering has bought me into contact with real people with real problems and I have really got to know quite a lot of people.

When I left Marie Curie as a volunteer to work as Parish Administrator, I was keen to remain in contact with them and, in December 2001, the idea of organising a Christmas Tree Festival in our church to raise money for the church and Marie Curie came to me as a way to combine the two. By December 2002, when I had been the organiser of Hertford's first Christmas Tree Festival for a year, it bore fruit and £3,400 was split between the two!

Although I organised it, almost single-handed, I had a fantastic amount of support from friends and family who all pitched in to make it such a success. Despite all the panic attacks and migraines I suffered as a result, the face of one small boy which lit up, when 40 sets of Christmas tree lights came on, will be an abiding memory. The pleasure it gave to so many people made it all worthwhile. I was presented with a "Gold Star" from the Rector and his wife and I received a superb letter of thanks from the Mayor of Hertford which my mother urged me to frame to mark my achievement.

Somehow, I knew it would not end there and in 2004 I organised another Christmas Tree Festival. It raised £3,800 which was split between the church and the Lavender Trust (a breast care charity for young women). However, in June 2004, my mother died suddenly and I had another bout of illness. So although the achievement may have been even greater, it was tinged with a great deal of sadness for me as she was not alive to see it and to share it. I knew it had to go ahead as my mother always faced deaths with the attitude that "life must go on" and somehow that determination manifested itself in me... the festival must go on...and it was a legacy I could not ignore.

14. The death of my mother – two more weeks of hell

My mother, though desperately worried about my illness, always believed "life must go on". She always kept busy and never allowed herself to wallow in self-pity – a very valuable lesson. Photograph by Barry Pywell.

Looking back now the death of my mother was strangely similar to the death of my father. She was taken ill on June 19 and died on June 30 – completely unexpectedly.

She stayed with my sister for two days initially when she was ill but then she came to stay with us because my sister had just lost her father-in-law to cancer and she was very busy dealing with the aftermath of that. During her stay, despite having "a stomach bug", she was her usual resilient self and although it was obvious she was very ill, we shared lots of "quality time" together. We laughed a lot and we reminisced and she made light of feeling awful. She even got dressed and came out "window shopping" with me. She sat in the car looking at clothes saying "when I'm feeling better, I'll try that jacket

60

on" such was her fighting spirit! Two days later she collapsed through dehydration and I called an ambulance and she was rushed to hospital. When she first arrived at A & E she was very positive, but once she was admitted, she seemed to go down hill quite fast.

I was studying with the University of Wales at the time for a Certificate in Interpersonal Skills for Volunteers and I was working on the chapter about assertiveness. Mother was adamant I should continue my studies and I found myself putting theory into practice.

No one seemed to know what was wrong with my mother. All the tests showed nothing but she did not improve. She was still being assessed but she seemed to be being treated as if she had dementia. Obviously I was upset and I went and had a cup of tea and shed some tears and then I started to be assertive. I asked to see the nurse in charge and I presented her with a list of questions and one of facts. I demanded that my mother's name be put on the door of her ward and that someone actually consider the facts and answer the questions. The result was quite astonishing.

The sister made me another cup of tea and sat down with me and talked the whole thing through. I made it very clear that without her glasses my mother could not see and without her hearing aid she could not hear! I also pointed out that mother was demanding to know what was wrong. It was 26 June and it was decided to do an exploratory operation. Mother gave consent to be kept on life support for 48 hours. While waiting to go into surgery she "communicated" with my sister and me all sorts of valuable information and we laughed a lot both with her and at her frustrations. She was on oxygen, without her glasses or hearing aid and with a nurse who had a limited command of English. Despite this, mother would not be beaten! She had always loved crosswords and our last few hours with her involved a lot of cryptic messages which my sister and I solved. Her last message stumped us both, but I think she would probably be rather pleased about that!

The surgery found nothing but the consultant felt that a further operation might just save her. Her kidneys and bowel were now failing. So we consented to another operation, and another 48 hours on life support, after which the life support machine was turned off and she died very peacefully.

In a strange way I was relieved and pleased. My mother had always feared growing old. Her father had gone blind; her mother had developed senile dementia and her brother had suffered from cancer – she was terrified of losing her independence and she didn't. Less than two weeks before she died, she was still working in the charity shop, mowing her lawns, doing her ironing and enjoying a gin and tonic and she was 79!

By early morning on 2 July, my euphoria about her death and the stress of her illness had taken its toll of me and I rang Dr Cembala who came out to see me. I knew I was in danger of another manic episode, as the treatment he had been giving me seemed to be having little effect. He and I had a rather bizarre interlude during which I thought I had agreed to be hospitalised, but he clearly thought I was no longer capable of giving rational consent and he had no choice but to have me sectioned. Clearly this is part of his job which he dreads...but so it was and the cavalry arrived once again: police, a social worker, another doctor and an ambulance. Just when I wanted to be allowed to grieve with what was left of my family, I was locked up in a mental health unit in a ward overlooking the room in which my mother had died. Sometimes life's a bitch!

As usual I was angry with the system and when I pointed out the irony of my situation, I was moved to a male ward! Have you ever tried to rest in a psychiatric unit in an un-lockable room surrounded by mentally ill males? I did, and I swear it is not possible even with sleeping tablets!

I was exhausted physically, emotionally and spiritually. At one point I collapsed and was physically sick on the carpet: one of the nurses accused me of making a mess and told me I would have to clear it up! This was compassion in England in 2004. Sometimes life beggars belief. I was, and am, lost for words.

I endured two weeks of hell but I did "respond to the medication" and was discharged on July 13. My mother's funeral was on July 14 and, although I hate speaking in public, I read one her favourite poems. Just as well I like a challenge!

I knew then that both my parents would have been very proud of me. My father was very fond of saying "Nil carborundum illegitimi" (which he always translated as "Don't let the b*******s grind you down"). Without a doubt, surviving that episode was the greatest achievement I have made since giving birth and, as I have said, six months later I pulled off another Christmas Tree Festival.

As we left church when it was all over, I swear I could hear a chuckle in the breeze and a distant voice muttering "You see, you don't know what you can do 'til you try!"…

15. Loving, hating and lashing out

When I was about 10, my maternal grandmother began suffering from senile dementia. She lived very close to us and my mother visited her twice a day most days. One of the things I remember most clearly about her mental deterioration was how she could become really vicious to my mother. There were times when she would come round to our house, in a confused state, in the middle of the night, expecting her dinner, and my mother would try and take her home to bed but she would become quite aggressive and often only my father could placate her and persuade her to go home with him. This was totally out of character as she and my mother had always been very close.

Now, unlike my grandmother, I grew up as a fiery red-head and spent many years learning to control my temper, so I cannot pretend that I am a stranger to lashing out orally but it is certainly not something I have made a habit of during my adult years.

I had known my future husband as a friend, for almost a year before we even went out together as a couple, and I remember being amazed at how quiet and placid he was. He once told me that he was quite shy and when he was with me he had no need to speak because I talked so much. (Some things don't change!)

However, since the onset of my illness, when I get really angry I go quiet. I will often burst into tears too, but my frustration and anger does eventually boil over and, of course, it is those closest to me, and those I love most, who bear the brunt of my tongue. My fuse is shorter and I am less tolerant of silly things which really don't matter.

As I have said before, I am extremely lucky to have survived the last 16 years, especially with my marriage intact, and that is in no small part due to the fact that I married this extremely placid, calm and emotionally stable man, who believes that marriage is "for better, for worse, for richer, for poorer, in sickness and in health". He is by no means perfect, but his attitude to me and my illness would take some beating!

On our 15th wedding anniversary he bought me a crystal 'book' called "Always" which came with a card that read: "When I said I do, I meant I do. I meant I will, I meant I always will" which sums up his philosophy of marriage. Despite his quietness he has a wonderful sense of humour which often allows him to defuse my anger.

When I am ill, and lashing out at him, he blames the illness, not me. For some reason every time I have been sectioned I have blamed him for having me locked up. Even after my mother died, when I rang my GP myself, I blamed him for me ending up in hospital with nothing but what I was standing up in! On that occasion, I was sectioned 19 years to the day since we got engaged and it certainly wasn't the way I would have chosen for us to spend the day.

In the past, when I have been sectioned, I have given him my wedding and engagement rings back and I have told staff that I don't wish to see him – I have punished him over and over again – and yet on a day-today basis he is the best, most stabilising influence in my life and we almost never argue!

Obviously I find it hard to accept that I lash out at him in this way but it seems to be beyond my control. I have wondered whether it is because we are forced to be apart, at a time that I feel I really need his help and support that I do it. I can't blame the entire cavalry which arrives to section me as they disappear into thin air but he is always there to pick up the pieces and coax me back to normality.

My GP is much the same, I would love to blame him for having me sectioned, but once I am locked up he disappears until I am discharged. When I have questioned him about it, he too says "it's in the past, let bygones, be bygones" and he usually finds a way to make me laugh and move on. The bottom line is I hate the illness and what it does to me, but as he says "it is an illness, if it were diabetes, you would hate that too" and I know he is right.

In the longer term, I take comfort from the way my grandmother used to behave towards the daughter she loved dearly, and from the fact that many people suffering from mental illnesses also "turn against" those closest to them and those who care for them the most.

Just as I try not to dwell too much on the effect of my illness on my life, rather get on with living it, so my husband and I rarely look back at the worst times, we try and live in the present.

On a practical note, I have now made a list of items I would like brought to me if I am sectioned again and given it to my sister, my closest friend, and told my daughters where they can find a copy. By doing this, I hope that I will not be able to level "being locked up with nothing but what I am standing up in" at him again.

Footnote: *If you, or someone close to you, is suffering from manic depression, it might be worth trying to find ways to make the worst parts easier when they are in a calm and rational frame of mind.*

My worst case scenario is that my husband will die suddenly and I will be sectioned. I have also made a Power of Attorney so that someone else could deal with my affairs if necessary. For a long time I have "put off" facing my worst fears and discussing them with my family but now that I have, I feel better about it.

16. Picking up the pieces and facing the future – learning to ignore labels – working for Rethink

If you had asked me three years ago about my worst fears, one of them would have been losing my mother and having to sell the house which had been my home since I was three months old. I was very close to my mother, we were very similar in looks and temperament and coincidentally her birthday was the day after mine! (For many years, as a child, I was puzzled as to how I could have been born the day before her, I didn't realise then that there was about 30 years between us, but then maths never was my strong point!)

However awful the death of my mother was, and the hospital stay which followed, it was not as bad as I feared. I came out of the mental health unit totally focussed on her funeral the next day and that gave me a purpose. I was also almost half way through my university course and through planning the Christmas Tree Festival, so I had plenty to focus on. Because my mother had been so supportive both of my studying and the festival, I knew I must complete both. In September my sister and I cleared out our family home and put it on the market and on September 29 I sent off my final assignment. From then on I tackled the festival with gusto.

In saying this, I missed my mother greatly and still do. She was a tremendous support to me. She would arrive and do the ironing, gardening or cleaning, anything to make me take a break, but she was also an excellent role model. I look back to when my father died and she was so ill, and I wonder how she coped. At the time she said: "Life must go on. I must pick up the pieces and face the future" and so she did. As I have said she made herself busier than ever – if she had time on her hands, you would find her sewing a tapestry or battling with a jigsaw puzzle – her secret, she told me, was never to let herself wallow in self-pity.

I decided that the best tribute I could pay to her was to try and do the same. It has not always been easy, I know she didn't ever profess it was easy, but I have tried to pick up the pieces and face the future without too much self-pity. I was thrilled to get a Distinction in my studying but deeply saddened that my mother couldn't be with me when I received my certificate. (She hated hats, but she had been joking with me while she was ill, that I must finish the course so that she could treat herself to a hat for the presentation ceremony!) I tried to persuade my tutor to post the certificate to me, but she was reluctant and, in the end, I went to the University of Wales at

The Vice Chancellor presenting me with my Certificate in Interpersonal Skills for Volunteers at the University of Wales, Lampeter. Photograph courtesy of Matthew Scott

Lampeter for two days with my husband (who bought a new suit!).

My mother was fond of saying "as one door closes, so another opens" and in my case the "hat door" closed, but another opened as a result of my trip to Lampeter. We had a formal dinner on the first evening and I was seated next to the keynote speaker for presentation day - a lady called Jean Thompson who founded the Expert Patients Programme in this country. Now I had no idea who she was, or what the EPP was about, but suffice it to say EPP is for people with long-term health conditions and so I was very interested. The programme aims to help them learn new ways to manage their conditions. I have now been on the course, which consists of one half day over six weeks, and I have also been on a three day residential course and qualified as a volunteer tutor!

Almost certainly as a result of my studying at Lampeter, I got a paid job, with the charity Rethink, one day a week, working at a drop-in centre for people with severe mental illness. This was a real challenge for me but I thoroughly enjoyed it.

I introduced silk painting, which was very popular and successful, and I met some of the most interesting people I have ever been privileged to know. Each one of them has a far more interesting story to tell than mine, and I was greatly inspired by their courage in the face of day-to-day challenges. Just walking down the street some of them would be intimidated because they stood out from the crowd. Going on buses was out of the question during school runs because the kids would call them names...I could go on...but still they came to the centre where they were treated with dignity and kindness. Part of my job was to cook for the members on a rota basis – to be honest I found this far more stressful than befriending them!

Unfortunately, six months to the day that I started, there was an aggressive incident, triggered by a member of the public with a deep dislike of the drop-in centre, which undermined my confidence to such an extent that I left. I felt very guilty about leaving all the lovely but vulnerable people I had met, but I knew I must look after myself first.

The job had been a real eye-opener. I had never taken much notice of labels before, but through working with so many people whose diagnoses were so different, but whose symptoms were often very similar, it confirmed to me that what mattered was not the diagnosis but the person. Although I am not writing this as a direct result of my work there, it enabled me to look at my own illness in a much wider context. Without a doubt, had I not experienced mental illness myself I could not have done the job and if I had not met so many very special people my life would be much poorer.

17. Keep fit, keep taking the tablets and hope for the best

Before I went on the Expert Patients Programme I had bought myself an exercise machine. It is nothing elaborate, but it folds away neatly and allows me to get regular exercise without leaving the house! I had given up swimming and going to the gym because there were too many excuses I could make not to go, but I can find far fewer excuses to not spend half an hour exercising at home! It is basically a walking machine which causes minimal impact to my back.

I find that exercise is very good for me, especially in the morning and, although I can't pretend I enjoy it, by listening to music (**not** Michael Ball) I find it is quite relaxing. I really feel more energised and positive about the day so I have taken to getting out of bed, putting on a track suit or shorts and a T-shirt and doing half an hour on my machine before I shower and dress, and so far I have kept it up two or three times a week, most weeks, for six months.

One of the problems with the Lithium Carbonate is that I have put on weight. I now weigh the same as I did when I was carrying the twins, 17 years ago, but I have lost half a stone in the last six months so the exercise regime is making me feel better in more ways than one!

Interestingly one of the modules on the EPP course looks at how exercise can help in the management of long-term health conditions, another looks at diet and I have been trying to take my diet in hand too.

I know that when I am depressed I eat for comfort; when I am manic I eat because I feel I need all the energy I can get; and otherwise I eat when I am bored or just because I like food! So I am trying to be much stricter about what, and when, I eat because I do realise it is important.

I have mentioned that I keep taking the tablets and I do, but I have tried to change my attitude to them. I used to regard them with disdain, almost as if they were poison. I think, because I took almost no medication before the onset of my illness, the concept of medication was fairly alien to me and I felt I should not need it, so I resented it and its side effects. Now I try and look on it as a valuable tool to help keep me well. I have a very pro-active approach to my illness now. I make sure I never run out of my medication and I keep a diary and make a note of my ups and downs and when my next check-up or next blood test is due and I remind my GP. It may sound silly, but it all makes me feel more in control of my illness.

Since the onset of my illness I have been hoping for the best and trying not to think about the worst, but now I am actively trying to be more positive in my outlook. I realised, while I was doing the EPP course, just how negative I had become. Each week on the programme we were encourage to make an "Action Plan", which was something we really wanted to achieve, and I set myself a target of thinking positively for just 15 minutes a day. I was surprised at how hard I found it but I did it and I have been working on positive thinking ever since. Over the years I have regularly felt defeated by very small things and I have felt unable to commit myself to anything because the illness had undermined my confidence to such an extent. The EPP course really helped to boost my confidence and my self-esteem and, one of my tutors, Julie Dennison, inspired me to write this book. She lives with epilepsy that is not controlled fully by drugs and she has written a book about living with her condition, so when I told her I was writing a book she was very encouraging, supportive and helpful.

At the end of the course we were encouraged to make a longer term goal and mine was to overcome my fear of flying. Since then I have planned a family holiday in Tuscany, which is now less than two weeks away. My daughters will finish their GCSE's next week and I wanted us all to have a really good break. This will be the first time I have flown any distance since they were born and, despite all my positive thinking, it is still quite daunting. I know that being sectioned has made me really claustrophobic and it is not taking off and landing I fear, it is feeling trapped in an aeroplane above the clouds. I know I will do it but I will be very glad when it is behind me!

Perhaps, if I write anything else it should be called "Tuscany and beyond!"

As I found the Expert Patients Programme so valuable, I thought I would include a few basic details about it:

It is a national initiative developed in America and founded in this country in 2002 to help people living with long term health conditions maintain their health and improve their quality of life through lay-led self-management courses. The courses are available **FREE** to anyone with a long-term health condition.

Feed-back so far suggests:

- Participants have greater confidence in dealing with their illness
- Experience less pain and fatigue, depression and anxiety
- Persevere with exercise and relaxation techniques
- Make fewer visits to the GP
- Visit A & E departments less often
- Enjoy better communication with health professionals

Courses are run at local venues all over the country.

For more information contact:
www.expertpatients.nhs.uk if you are not on the internet, ask your GP, local hospital or library if they can find details for you.

NB Current in 2007

18. A blessing in disguise – compassionate teenagers!

Elsewhere in the book I have paid tribute to my husband and the way he has dealt with my illness but in this last chapter I would like pay tribute to my daughters. As the problems all started with their birth, it feels right to come full circle and end by talking about them.

As I have said, they were probably the single most important factor in my fighting to stay alive and, through all my mental torment, they have been a very positive reason to keep going.

When they were quite little and I was having a bad day they would say "mummy want chocolate?" as they grew older they would say "Mum needs a cup of tea (and/or) an emergency Mars bar!" Now they tend to offer to give me a manicure or to blow-dry my hair although they do ask if I need retail therapy too! Just before Christmas 2005 life was very stressful and they were "winding me up" and to quote them "I went off on one!" and had a lie down with Michael Ball. When I surfaced there was a note of apology and two mini Mars bars from a box of Celebrations sitting by the bed.

We have always been honest with them about my illness and we have never pretended that one day everything would be lovely again. That said, neither have we painted the future as very black. We have tried to explain that I suffer from a difficult and complicated illness but with their help we will cope and so we have.

They have learned to cope throughout all the ups and downs and they have developed their own mechanisms for dealing with me. Generally we have a very close relationship, but when I nag one of them or get angry with one they tend to unite against me! I know this is not uncommon with any children and certainly not twins but there have been times when I have blamed my illness for this.

Over the years I have worried a great deal about the effect my illness would have on them and sometimes when they are really angry with one another or me, I fear they are emulating me on a bad day! I remember one health professional telling me when they were very young that they would learn my behaviour and develop both manic and depressive tendencies from me - that really thrilled me!

I have to say, partially because of this, I was dreading the teenage years but, although I would never pretend they have been easy, so far, we are not half as hysterical and dysfunctional as I feared we would be.

The girls are very protective of me. They are very well attuned to my needs and they still have a very close relationship with their father. What surprises me even more is how many other people comment on how kind and helpful they are and how unusual it is to find not one, but two, teenagers who are lovely! Usually I do query if they mean my two, but I think that because they have seen suffering at close hand, they instinctively care about the "underdog". They have brokered a number of peace deals in relationships at school and have become actively involved, through their school, in a community project involving drug addicts and alcoholics. Their attitude has been really interesting. Like me, they have been more concerned with the individuals than the problems they have. They accept that just as anyone can become mentally ill, so anyone can become a drug addict or an alcoholic. The staff member in charge said he could not speak too highly of their attitude!

Not surprisingly then, they are extremely patient and loving towards their grandmother who is now 91 and suffering from senile dementia. They have friends with special needs and they automatically make allowances for their problems. One elderly lady summed them up by saying they were very compassionate, and that seems to me to be a very positive spin-off from my illness, which has to have been a blessing in disguise!

My daughters in 2007

Having said all that, they are by no means perfect, but I love them dearly, and if they leave home in two years it will be very quiet without them and I shall have to make sure I don't become "a sad old woman" and make sure I "get a life or whatever!"

Some practical help for Depression

Whether or not you are on medication, it might be worth trying the following:

Breathing exercises

As you breathe in, and as you hold the breath, visualise that all this new, fresh, air is giving you new and positive energy. As you breathe out, slowly force out as many dark, sad and depressing thoughts as you can to make room in your body for the new ones. Do this as often as you can. There is no life without breath and when you are depressed breathing often becomes shallow and laboured. If you feel like sighing in despair or frustration, think, as you do it, that all that negativity is leaving you and making room for your life to become more positive.

Did you know that when you cry tears are healing? You don't always need "a shoulder to cry on". Crying alone can be helpful. Accepting and releasing the emotion is a way of managing your distress. Letting tears flow washes out pain and, when you cry, your body releases tension and toxins and this helps to rebalance your emotions. When you cry, try not to cry for too long as this may well make you look and feel awful. (I know I always end up with a blotchy red face and nose and a splitting headache!) Afterwards try washing your face in cold water, to reduce the redness, and then (if you are female) put on some make-up so you can face the world from behind a mask then go outside and speak to someone. (Even if you only comment on the weather, it will help you move on.)

This often works for me. I hope it works for you.

Postscript

Many years ago, long before my illness began, I remember reading that an opal is only made of sand and silica and it is nothing until it is broken and the light gets in and lets it emit the most beautiful rays. I have an opal in my engagement ring and I often wonder if, as humans, when we have been broken by mental illness, especially manic depression, we get a more beautiful perspective on life....

Tuscany and Beyond
a Recovery Journey

Contents

"The recovery model aims to help people with mental illnesses and distress to look beyond mere survival and existence. It encourages them to move forward and set new goals. It supports the view that they should get on with their lives, do things and develop relationships that give their lives meaning." [Author unknown}

Over the last fourteen years I hope this is what I have done...

Tuscany and beyond...a recovery journey

Publishing *Double Trouble* in 2007 was fraught with anxiety. Not least because the publisher sadly died suddenly at the final proof stage and I was left alone to manage the launch and the sales.

Eric Vernon Scott the publisher of Double Trouble – very at home in his editorial office.

I say "launch" but I had two launches in the end because the first was at a very small venue, chosen for that very reason, but so many people wanted to come that I held a second a week later at my church.

I was featured in a whole page article in the local press and contacted by Premier Christian Radio who wanted to interview me live on a show. Life was manic and I began to fear that I would be sectioned again. I turned down the radio interview and went to my GP. (I have learnt over the years that getting help early is vital. The medication takes time to kick in but my mental state deteriorates in hours not days)

I was manic. Many things were going through my mind as they do when you are manic but I had an overriding fear that I would not sell the 500 books that had been delivered to my home. The book's sponsor's, Sanofi Aventis, had received their 1,000 copies but I had the rest in the garage. (The original plan had been to print 2,500 but without the publisher, and his storage space, I cut it by 1,000.)

Somewhere along the line, in the week or so while waiting for the medication to take effect, I decided that I had better give talks to local organisations,, as well as marketing the book online. The former was a big deal for me as I hate public speaking but I felt that only I could tell my story and encourage people to buy the book and read more of it. Online I was more out of my depth and I spent a considerable amount of money on having a website designed and launched and on someone who promised much and delivered little by way of improving my take up rate. However we live and learn. What I did learn was that the book was of interest to clergy who, with the demise of inpatient beds, had to deal with numerous people suffering from mental illness. I started e-mailing clergy and had a good take-up rate. I also did a number of talks, mainly to small local groups and found, along with those sold on the website, they were disappearing. In two years they were all gone.

Among the many I sent as complimentary copies was one to the Hertfordshire Partnership University NHS Foundation Trust (the mental health provider for this area and known simply as HPFT or The Trust). This came to the attention of the Chaplain and we arranged to meet. Little did I know then that it was, along with a small advertisement in a church publication, to shape the next eight years of my volunteering life. In 2011 I became a spiritual care volunteer for the Trust and have worked with the chaplaincy team ever since.

The book has found its way to all sorts of places, including Australia, and the feedback has been mainly positive. Apparently it has helped families understand the illness and, in that respect, it has fulfilled my wish. When I was first ill, with a diagnosis of manic puerperal psychosis, my father searched desperately for information about the illness and drew a blank. I wanted to fill that gap.

Now, fourteen years later, the date of April 12 2007 is etched on my heart. It is the date of my first book launch. The Venue was Courtyard Arts in Hertford. I chose this because it was small and intimate and I feared no one would turn up. How wrong I was everyone I had invited came, and a few more too.

The catering was organised and glasses hired. I had an outfit and ridiculously high shoes and the stage was set with a pile of books. Cllr Peter Ruffles kindly agreed to introduce the proceedings and I had a short speech all prepared.

To say I was nervous was putting it mildly; guests included former colleagues from the public relations world, three former teachers, the Mayor of Hertford, and friends from all walks of life. One memorable highlight was that my brother-in-law was present. He had just finished six months of chemotherapy and I promised not to crack open the Champagne unless he was there, and he was.

**Me at my book launch.
Photo by Alison Adler**

It was a very special event made even more nerve wracking when a member of the press arrived to interview me and take photos. I think the photographs unnerved me more than anything – I prefer to be behind the camera. The result of this was a full page spread in the local paper and a phone call the following day for a further interview. I was literally lying in a darkened room suffering from migraine when the call came through but I knew I had to function as a professional author and I did my best. The launch took a lot out of me emotionally and physically but I had committed myself to a second launch on 18 April, just six days later.

I was more relaxed about the second launch, but it was at my church which is a bigger venue and I had made an open invitation to members of the church to attend, so it promised to be more out of my control. I am a control freak, so this worried me. However our vicar introduced the evening and I made a short speech and it all began. Sales went well and everyone wanted to talk. It was a success and when it was all over I was on a high.

Now most people would be on a high after a week like that but mine was a dangerous high. With bipolar disorder (or manic depression as I prefer to call it) emotions cause all sorts of side effects. The world seems brighter, everything seems perfect and I begin to imagine that the TV and the radio are talking to me. Alarms bells start ringing and I know I need help, and quickly.

My GP who had been at the first launch sent a community psychiatric team round and they reassured me that if I took my increased medication I would not be sectioned. Over a cup of tea this was all discussed very calmly and I battened down the hatches to ride it out. Having previously been sectioned four times, and knowing how dehumanising the experience was, I was keen to avoid it at all costs and so I did.

Gradually life began to settle down and I returned to some semblance of normality. Book sales trickled on and I started giving a few talks about my book.

The Tuscany Trip

The summer of 2006 saw my daughters, Jenny and Helen, complete their GCSEs, and a heatwave across Europe. Temperatures were regularly in the high 30s centigrade and, despite my fear of flying, we made it to Tuscany as a family. We got lost on the way to the villa we were renting, and my family have fond memories of me asking directions in loud clear English and getting a response in fast spoken Italian, However I confidently said we need to go round the corner and turn left and sure enough we found the villa. It was beautiful, with its own pool, and wooden shutters which kept out the sun. I mention this because it was the pool and the shutters that got me through the holiday. (I am not good in heat and have even had sunstroke in Clacton.) We had a lovely family holiday and, although we didn't go out much, we did visit the Leaning Tower of Pisa and a wonderful old church in Barga which provided much needed respite from the heat..

However on the last morning I slipped down the steps in the bathroom and damaged my right ankle. So when we were stranded for about four hours on the tarmac at Pisa airport my ankle began to swell. We were taxiing ready for take off when a lady was taken ill and we had to offload her and baggage, hence the delay. For someone who dislikes flying the delay was very stressful and by the time we took off I was close to a panic attack and in

Nigel and I outside the Villa in Tuscany.

considerable pain. Anyone who has experienced a
panic attack will know that you don't want to have
one in public. Stuck on a plane is the very last place
I would choose. However I used my Bach's Rescue
Remedy spray and took some painkillers and with a
lot of deep breathing somehow I got through. her

9

The death of OM (my mother-in-law)

Shortly afterwards we had a French exchange student to stay. I dropped my daughters and the student off for a trip to London and my mobile phone went off. This was an unusual occurrence then because few people had my number, so I stopped to answer it, only to find it was the Nursing Home looking after my mother-in-law to say she was very ill and unlikely to survive the day.

I drove to the home (about 45 minutes away) with mixed emotions. I loved my mother in law dearly and she had been fantastic with me throughout the darkest days of my illness, but she was 92 and had been suffering from senile dementia for the past eight years. In a sense she was already lost to us but then again, she was still with us in body.

When I entered her room I knew she was near the end. She had a terrible cough, which I believe is known as a death rattle, and she was in and out of consciousness. I tried desperately to contact my husband and his brother but both were miles away for work. However I kept hugging her and telling her they would soon be here and they both arrived within minutes of each other at lunchtime. She literally greeted them both and breathed her last.

When I say she was fantastic to me during my illness, I do not exaggerate. While my parents looked after my twin daughters, my mother-in-law looked after me. She confided that she had suffered from post natal depression after the birth of her first son, so she had some idea of my state of mind. Having spent three months in hospital when the girls were 16 months old, I came home still depressed and practically institutionalised. She coaxed me to get out of bed; she coaxed me to get dressed; she coaxed me to put on clothes; to put on make-up and leave the house.

Helen and Jenny with OM at 90!

This may sound simple but it all took weeks and months. In the meantime, keen that I should eat well, she cooked meals to put in the freezer and encouraged me to reheat them. We had always shared a love of cooking and together we began to cook again.

Despite shaking from head to foot, I gave a long eulogy to my OM (other mother) at her funeral because I felt I should pay tribute to an amazing lady. (I wish I had known about beta blockers then because I would not have been so jelly-like.)

University and an empty nest

Jenny and Helen left home in 2008 to go to University. Jenny went to Southampton to read Chemistry and Maths and Helen went to Liverpool to read English and French. The build up was quite chaotic. I recall bags and boxes everywhere but I included a tin of flapjack each on the grounds that students are always hungry. In Liverpool I sat on Helen's bed all alone in her room and felt awful. It took me back to the mother and baby unit in the mental health wing when they were babies and I hated it. (I had been sectioned and could only take one baby – so I took neither and went alone.) I also remember visiting Paddy's Wigwam (the Roman Catholic Cathedral) and offering a silent prayer for Helen.

In Southampton I remember loud music greeted us and I felt very alienated from everything. Having never been to university it was all new to me and I wasn't sure that I wanted to entrust my daughters to this way of life, but I had no choice. I gather that the flapjacks went down well and they both made friends quickly – some of them are still in touch.

At university the girls both flourished. They both joined the Officer Training Corps (OTC) and took part in lots of adventurous pursuits. Jenny joined the orchestra and became secretary of the Southampton University Symphony Orchestra and we enjoyed numerous concerts in which she played the oboe. However it was the OTC which struck a chord with her and to this day she is a member of the Royal Engineers Army Reserve .

For my own part I tried to fill the empty nest and I enrolled Nigel and me in pottery classes, which proved a lot of fun. Our teacher was an elderly gentleman who let us do whatever we liked, and I found I liked making a mess and filling the recycling bin. I had never touched clay before and he was keen for me to experiment. Meanwhile Nigel, who had done pottery before, proved very good at slab work and made a number of items including a canal boat. The highlight for me was making, with the help of another member of the group, a wok bowl

"The Blue Pool" as the bowl has become known.

which was moulded between two woks. I filled it with broken glass beads and glazed it turquoise. It came out so well that it was exhibited and apparently would have sold, but I didn't want to part with it. I shall never know how rich I could have been. It still has pride of place on my dining room table and is testament to the fact that it is worth trying something new.

Another highlight of the year was the Hertfest Awards and I was nominated for having the courage to write and publish my book. To my amazement I won, and received a beautiful glass trophy from an elderly lady at our church who had nominated me and sponsored the trophy. She had sat with me in church when my publisher died and held my hand so she had some idea how deeply I felt the loss. I was very touched by it and made a very short speech in which I said I was receiving it on behalf of all those suffering from mental illness who were less fortunate than me. Again the trophy sits in pride of place in my lounge – and since her passing, serves as a reminder of a very faithful lady who made it happen.

Earlier on I mentioned that my book came to the attention of the Chaplain for HPFT, and it coincided with me seeing an advert for spiritual care volunteers in a church publication. It said words to the effect: "No experience required, just a faith base, some experience of mental illness and a listening ear." The contact details led you to the Chaplain at HPFT.

I saw this advert and thought "that sounds like me," but did nothing about it. Then, after two other people had pointed it out to me, I contacted her and we arranged a meeting. She explained that this was a new initiative and that training would be offered starting in September. I gave this a lot of thought and then committed to it. It was another attempt to fill the empty nest and have a purpose in life. Many years before, when I had taken on the job of parish administrator at our church, I remember thinking it was a kind of "calling" and taking this on felt much the same.

The day the training started I was to be picked up by another volunteer that I had never met outside St Andrew's church in Hertford. If you know St Andrew Street at all you will know it is quite a busy road and I stood there peering into cars that might be going to stop in the hope that one would. What seemed like an eternity later a car pulled up with two ladies inside, and I met Jose and Monika for the first time. Jose was the wife of a vicar who wanted her own little ministry, and Monika was Polish and wanted to work with adults with special needs and learning disabilities. I didn't really know what I wanted or what to expect, but something was telling me I should explore this "calling".

We arrived at the car park in Radlett unsure where to go and were greeted by a lovely man called Alan who said "Don't follow me, I'm lost too" and we discovered he was looking for the same building, indeed the same course. He was a lovely character who was involved in setting up a church abroad but wanted to work with the elderly when he was in England. He and his colleague Bernie eventually became "Victoria and Elizabeth" on account of the wards where they worked. Bernie was based at the church where I was baptised and we all got on very well.

Because the training was held in Radlett, Josie Monika and I had plenty of time to talk in the car and the journey time became special. I think there were about 12 of us to start with and the course was run by the Chaplain, Verity, and Linda, a volunteer Chaplain. The latter was a wonderful, warm, bouncy character who made everyone feel at ease. (It turned out she was a twin, and during the course I met her twin sister which was really lovely for me.)

The horror (and shame) of handcuffs

During the course I started suffering from migraines again. Throughout my adult life I had suffered regularly, as has had my mother and grandmother, and there was a distinct pattern of deep pain over the left eye and violent sickness. This episode lasted five days (the longest I can ever remember) and resulted in me suffering a manic episode because I was not keeping my medication down. Now when I'm manic, although many things are very vivid, because my brain is playing tricks on me, other things are a bit of a blur. I remember needing a GP (mine was on holiday) and being convinced that I needed a blood test. Somewhere along the line I got up and got dressed and took myself to Hertford County Hospital in the hope of getting one. (Had I been rational I would have known I needed a form from my GP but my thinking was flawed and the relevant department was shut anyway). So I headed for the out of hours clinic and tried to explain the problem.

I was told that my consultant was in the building and that he would come and see me. This was the worst thing that could have happened. I have never got on with him and I think he had made a decision to section me before we even spoke. I remember feeling physically ill and putting my head out of the window for some fresh air and then I saw the bed and asked if I could lie down.

The next thing I recall is two police officers, one male and one female, by my side asking me to get up. I tried to stand but my legs gave way under me and they seemed to think I was being difficult so they handcuffed me and dragged me to a waiting police car. They left me handcuffed in the car and I felt like a criminal but my only crime was mental illness. I asked where they were taking me in the hope it would be home, but somehow I knew my life was unravelling again due to my illness.

We arrived at the (now demolished) mental health unit at QEII and I was subdued and injected; history was repeating itself and I felt desperately in need of some TLC. During this stay I was sick on the floor and one of the nurses told me I would have to clear it up. This was mental health care in 2009. and I felt it was very wrong. Two weeks later I was discharged and carried on with my spiritual care course believing that what was needed most was someone with time and empathy to sit and listen. However this episode of illness has scarred me deeply.

Ironically later the same year I was part of the interview process for the new CEO at Hertfordshire Partnership Foundation Trust, Tom Cahill. I don't recall what I asked him, but I do recall that I was very impressed with his answer. He had started his mental health career as a nurse and I remember thinking that if anyone could improve the service he could.

More positive things followed. I remember the opening of Mind in Mid Herts (MiMH) in Hertford by Alastair Campbell. I had wanted a mental health charity in Hertford ever since I had worked for Rethink in Ware and I was delighted when they found premises. MiMH was to play a part in my life for many years to come and I had a brief chat to Alastair about writing about mental illness, and he signed a copy of his book *All in the Mind* with the message "To Pauline Good luck and best wishes for the future. Keep on writing! Alastair Campbell".

I realise that by writing this book I am heeding his advice and that writing is good therapy. With my hobby of silk painting I make cards which I sell in aid of MiMH and I have raised several hundred pounds for them in this way.

Not long after they opened I was having a bad time mentally and my GP suggested cognitive behavioural therapy (CBT) but said there was a six month wait on the NHS. I went to MiMH and talked to them and they offered me the chance to start a six week "Fear Fighters" course online there and then. I actually started the following day, but it was better than I could have hoped. Each session was followed by a review with the manager of the charity and it gave me hope that I could conquer some of my demons.

Although I never completed the final challenge of looking ahead it was a very beneficial six weeks.

When I say I didn't complete the course I found the last challenge impossible. I was required to enter a dream and work out steps of how to achieve it. As someone who has spent much time learning to take one day at a time this stumped me. All I could think of was meeting Michael Ball, and I had no way of achieving that.

Much cause for celebration and the week from hell

In January 2010 on a very snowy day I was commissioned as a spiritual care visitor in a short church service. It was very moving. My vicar and the lady deacon (who had given me Communion so many years ago) joined with Cllr Ruffles and my husband and his brother to support me and, as I held the lighted candle, I remember feeling very at peace with myself.

I started volunteering at Seward Lodge, an older people's unit in Hertford, where I visited almost weekly for nearly six years. I feel it was making some good come out of the awfulness of mental illness.

In March I was 50. I organised a cheese and wine party at home for about 20 people but, with my friend Sandra, who I met as a bump when our mum's went to antenatal classes, we decided to celebrate with a trip called "We know who we are!". The idea for this came from the TV series *Who do you think you are?* We hired a 1960s Rolls Royce and did a tour of our past in Hertfordshire. We went to schools, churches, houses, and most importantly had lunch at the pub where we had our first legal alcoholic drink.

Sandra and I with the Rolls Royce on our 50th birthday tour.

It was a lovely day which ended with the four of our daughters making afternoon tea for us at my house. I thought I had celebrated well, but Nigel had booked a trip to Holland as a surprise for me with a visit to Keukenhof Park for the April. It was somewhere I had always wanted to go, and I loved it.

The next few months were spent planning our silver wedding party for the October. This was tinged with sadness because Helen was about to embark on her year abroad in Aix-en-Provence, and would be leaving the week before the party. However, in the event, we arranged for a Skype link so that she could "join us".

We booked Hertford Castle for afternoon tea and invited about 80 friends, some of whom had been at our wedding. It was very memorable and definitely "a sparkly bit".

In June we celebrated the silver wedding of two of our longstanding friends Mary and Chris. I had actually introduced them and been a bridesmaid at their wedding, so it was very special.

Less than a month later my world was to be turned upside down with a week from Hell.

On the Monday evening I was queuing for fish and chips as an end of term treat for our pottery class when I noticed some youths arguing. Before I realised it one had pulled a knife and stabbed the other in the neck. Various people went to help but I stood rooted to the spot unable to believe my eyes. The police set up an incident base near the shops and I did offer to tell them what I saw. However they said unless I actually saw the knife being pulled and used they didn't need my evidence. I gather the victim survived.

On the Friday evening, very unusually just before bed, I checked my emails and there was one from Mary. It said Chris had attempted suicide and was in hospital and would like to see me. I was stunned. I knew he had suffered from depression much of his adult life but never imagined he would attempt to take his own life. Apparently he had taken an overdose of antidepressants and cycled to work where he collapsed. He was taken to hospital by ambulance, but the medication had damaged his heart. Despite this thankfully he survived.

I visited him early on Saturday afternoon and practically yelled at him "What the bloody hell did you think you were doing?" I am not sure who was more surprised by my outburst, him or me, but it did lead to a useful dialogue. When he was discharged from hospital I kept a close eye on him and on one occasion after a walk we agreed I would take him to MiMH for some professional help. He found this beneficial and, with the acquisition of a dog, put him on the road to recovery. (Hence part of my gratitude to MiMH.)

As if that wasn't enough for one week on the following Monday I learnt that the son of a close friend had been diagnosed with a terminal brain tumour. He was considerably younger than me and it was another shock. I headed for my GP knowing that I was walking a tightrope of mental illness and it was being stretched to the limit.

My sleep pattern was shot to pieces and I kept shaking from head to foot. He increased my medication and I rode out the storm.

In October 2010 my GP of 23 years retired and left something of a hole in my life. He had diagnosed my illness all those years ago and had seen me through some very rough times. He had always had the philosophy than spending a few minutes on the phone to me was better that spending hours with me when I needed to be sectioned. He was going to be a hard act to follow, but life moves on and I had to move on too. If there is one thing that has been crucial to my recovery, it is the continuity with my GP. Even today, I am lucky enough to have regular appointments with the head of the practice and I shudder to think where I would be without them.

A bomber, beer and peanuts

Life settled down and the following spring Nigel and I spent a very special weekend in Lincolnshire, the highlight of which was attending a concert under the wing of a Lancaster bomber. My father had been stationed in Lincolnshire as ground crew working on Lancasters during the war and we were able to visit the Battle of Britain flight too. I think the Lancaster has a special place in my heart because when my father died Helen, who was then 4, said "Don't worry mummy he can go to heaven in a Lancaster." He always said they were his first love, my mother was a close second.

Easter that year was very memorable too. As a family we went to stay in France, in Aix-en-Provence where Helen was spending a year working on a dissertation about bilingual road signs. I can't begin to tell you how this came about but it was all part of her degree. We travelled by Eurostar, which was a first for me. I had serious misgivings about being in a tunnel under the sea for so long but in the event Jenny and Nigel distracted me with food and drink and, when we finally arrived in Aix, after more train journeys, I just wanted to lie down. As I lay on the bed I remember a wave of relief flooding over me and the sensation that my body was still moving. Although it was quite late at night we were all hungry and Helen introduced us to the 24-hour boulangerie! Only the French could come up with such a wonderful idea and we all enjoyed an impromptu picnic in our apartment. (Helen revisited Aix in 2019 and the boulangerie was no longer there – very sad.)

I don't travel well and I think I took some medication before I went to sleep and woke up feeling a lot better. My birthday treat from the girls had been a cookery lesson at a venue in Aix and all four of us enjoyed cooking salmon with a pink peppercorn sauce and then eating it. It was a "sparkly bit".

On Easter day I felt strange not going to church but we enjoyed a lovely leisurely day wandering round Aix and taking in the superb displays in the windows of chocolatiers and patisseries. For a chocoholic like me it was a little piece of heaven.

Before she came back from France, Helen was selected from the OTC, along with one other cadet in England, to join the French army for a month's training. We were very proud of her. She found it quite tough at times but, being the youngest soldier, it was her duty to get the day's rations and she was highly amused and delighted to discover that they included beer and peanuts. This was an unexpected pleasure. She passed out in July at a ceremony which started at midnight. Nigel and Jenny went out to watch and saw virtually nothing (I stayed at home to deal with a pest control man and a wasps' nest outside our bedroom window). I thought I had drawn the short straw but apparently there was a lot of singing and music and one green figure amongst a sea of blue. We asked her why they held the graduation ceremony at night and she said "I think it is because their drill is not very good so no one can see it!"

Tragedy and triumph

2012 started on a positive note. I knew Jenny and Helen would graduate and I decided to lose weight before July so that I could feel good about myself and treat myself to two new outfits. I joined Weight Watchers and started taking weight loss seriously for the first time in my life. One of the downsides of the medication I take is that it makes me put on weight, and, with a goal set, I was very focused. I even joined the group and was rewarded when I lost half a stone. In the end I lost almost one stone by July and bought two new outfits to celebrate.

The previous month Nigel retired after 38 years in the water industry. We had two retirement parties and I received two beautiful bouquets. However I wondered how, after 27 years of on-call stints and lots of long hours, we would find living together, and living together with my illness.

I had grown used to having the house to myself all day and now there was someone else to consider. We found new routines (which are so important to me) and I carried on with many of my old ones.

I think he has become more of a carer than a husband, but he disputes this – he says he is my husband so of course he cares. Because I have such awful mornings, he regularly brings me breakfast in bed. He also gives me lifts when I don't feel like driving and he asks me if I think I need extra medication when times are tough, and I know I am **very** lucky to have him.

Around this time, Jenny was looking for work and she spotted an advert for graduate trainees with Thames Water. Little did she know then that that was exactly where her father's career had started. After a long selection process she started work with them in September – we had managed almost three months without a member of the family in the water industry.

Most of the year passed unremarkably but tragedy struck on June 30. I was just going to bed when an ambulance man rang and asked if we could go to our friend Brian's house where his son, Robin, needed help. Nigel rushed off only to find our friend had had a massive heart attack and his son had found him unresponsive when he returned from University for the last time. It was a huge shock to us all. Sadly his mum had lost her battle with cancer when he was 6 so now he had lost both parents. Nigel stayed at the house all night and Robin came to stay with me. We tried to contact his sister Jacqui, who was abroad, and had little success initially. We tried watching TV. We drank tea. We cried. We talked. We sat in stunned silence. It was a long night but we decided that Robin would stay with us for a few days. Once his sister was on a plane home, we contacted other members of his family. His aunt and uncle came up from Dorset and his grandparents came from

Essex. I made lots of tea and coffee and tried to stay calm and in control. I contacted my GP and he increased my medication, and between us we arranged the funeral. It was with great sadness that we said goodbye to a dear friend who had come through so much with us.

To this day I like to think of Robin and Jacqui as extended family and try to be here for them when they need us. They are both lovely, well adjusted adults, which is a great testimony to their parents, especially their father.

Just four days after the funeral I found myself in Liverpool on a very wet day with no shoes. Helen was due to graduate and I had put my outfit on, only to find I had left my shoes behind. After much deliberation, we found a shoe outlet on a business park which was open at 9am and I rushed in, bought a pair of shoes and a pair of sandals and rushed out. The shoes were very uncomfortable but they were better than my walking boots.

I associate Liverpool with rain. On my 11th birthday one of my cousins got married in Liverpool. It was the first time I had ever been, and boy did it rain. Just over 40 years later as we walked from the Philharmonic Hall to the reception it did exactly the same. Umbrellas were definitely the order of the day.

Helen and I at her graduation.

However as I sat in the hall watching my daughter graduate with a 2:1 in English and French the weather was the last thing on my mind. I was very emotional. It was a day I never thought would come and it felt very special indeed. When you have mental illness there is a lot of grey in your life so when a "sparkly bit" comes along you need to treasure it and I did. Indeed I still do.

Nigel and I with Jenny on her graduation.

Exactly a week later I found myself in Southampton on a sunny day wearing sandals. The occasion was Jenny's graduation and it was in the Turner Sims Theatre at the University. It was a very hot day and I was fearing sunburn as we walked from the hall to the reception. It couldn't have been more different but this was tinged with a little sadness because Helen was not with us. She was studying at the University of Warwick for her Teach First qualification and so just the three of us celebrated this milestone. Jenny was one of two to graduate in Chemistry with Maths and she also got a 2:1. Once again I had a lump in my throat as I took stock of her achievement. I was humbled too by the thought that Brian would not see Robin graduate.

I felt strange when Robin did graduate with a first class honours degree in Engineering. Although I wasn't there I gather the auditorium erupted with cheers for him, and they were justly deserved.

Robin at his graduation and with Jacqui at hers two years later, in 2014, Jacqui graduated with a 2:1 in Economics from Swansea and Robin was a very proud brother!

A marathon effort, a BBC interview and a spa

The following April Jenny ran the London Marathon and I held a coffee morning to raise money for her. It was the first time I had sold my hand painted silk cards and I had spent hours making 80 to sell, and a long time baking cakes for a sale as well as the coffee morning; in the end I raised £250 towards her total.

Later that year I was a bag of nerves when I was interviewed live on 3 Counties Radio. I thought the interview was going to be about the new Mental Health Unit being built in Radlett and the Spiritual Care Team, but in the event they asked me mainly about my book. It was a strange way to spend a Sunday morning in a BBC radio studio in Luton, and one of the many experiences I never expected to have. When I listen to the recording I can still hear my voice shaking, but Karen the Chaplain was squeezing my hand all the way through and she said I sounded fine. (I have now served under four Chaplains and they have all been amazingly supportive in different ways.)

Because my birthday always falls near Mothering Sunday, Jenny and Helen have always treated me on a day of their choosing. So I never know when my day will be. However for my 25th Mothering Sunday they booked a spa day for all three of us and we went to the Gosling Sports Stadium where they have a spa pool with two steam rooms, a laconium, a sauna and water jets. This was wonderful – it was so good in fact that I later joined. I had often joked that what I needed more than being sectioned was a spa trip and it certainly helps my mood and refreshes me in a way nothing else does. Unfortunately the facilities were taken over and the membership cost doubled, so I am no longer a member but I do still treat myself as a non-member occasionally. (A friend and I try and go once a month but it doesn't always happen.)

Blowing my own trumpet

My fear of flying is never far away but in June 2014 we flew to Switzerland from Luton...well, we did after a six hour delay. During those six hours we did a good impression of a Benny Hill sketch. We were sent to a boarding gate only to be sent back again...again...and again. This was not helping my nerves at all and by the time we took off I was extremely anxious. When we arrived we took the train to Interlaken and it was during the journey that we found our mobile phones would not work. This added to my anxiety as we needed to tell the travel company that we had been delayed, or so I thought. In the event we arrived in Interlaken about 11pm to be greeted by a rep who had spotted our delay and tracked our connections. Never have I been so pleased to see a young man with a board in my life. He had also contacted the hotel and had arranged for food to be left in our room and offered us a mobile phone so we could call home. The company was Inghams, who Nigel had been skiing with before we were married and they scored 10/10 on Trip Advisor from us.

As we had arrived in the dark, opening the curtains in the morning was really amazing. We had a balcony overlooking the Aare river with the Eiger in the background. It was stunning! We had a fantastic holiday including a train ride to the Schynige Platte where I made friends with some alpenhorn players who let me have a go. It was quite surreal standing on a mountain blowing my own trumpet.

My alpenhorn friends!

A month later, Jenny and Helen and a group of friends did a Tough Mudder course and, after hosing them all down, I cooked them Sunday lunch. Only my daughters would enjoy an obstacle course including barbed wire and a water tank, or so I thought, but apparently the event was a sell out. Somehow this kind of pleasure has passed me by.

A new hospital and new Chaplains

While I was volunteering for HPFT I attended a number of meetings about the new hospital which was being built in Radlett. They were keen to get the opinion of a "service user" or, as I was otherwise known, "an expert by experience". My opinions were canvassed on all manner of things from furniture to paint to artwork. It was very interesting and reminiscent of my mother who worked on the supply section of the Lister Hospital in Stevenage when that was being built. I can remember her saying it was amazing how many toilet roll holders and towel dispensers a hospital needs.

I was also invited to be a part of the interview panel for the Chaplaincy department which was, of course, close to my heart. I forget how many applicants we interviewed but I know it took all day and we selected three.

I clearly remember a gentle Muslim lady named Yasmin, a former army padre called Terry and a C of E priest called Richard.
I thought they would make a good team, and I have been proved right. They have been wonderfully supportive colleagues of mine for almost four years and between them they have supported hundreds of service users through their darkest times.

Rev Richard Allen head of
Spiritual Care at HPTF

I have rung Richard and Terry when I have been at a low ebb and in need of a listening ear and they have been there for me. Without the Chaplaincy team my life would be much poorer.

Aside from all of this, Robin was running the London Marathon and I was frantically painting silk cards for a coffee morning to raise money for him. I forget how much I raised but I know that Robin calculated that I had spent much longer painting than he had running. It was my kind of marathon…sitting down with a cup of tea and some music, watching paint dry.

Just before the marathon, the new Lead Chaplain, Richard, started, and before long he had recruited me to join the Chaplaincy team as an expert by experience. This entailed going to team meetings once a month and giving the perspective of the patient on their discussions. It has been interesting and the team have made me very welcome. They, in particular, the Lead Chaplain, Richard, have encouraged me to tell my story and to use my experiences to help others.

In June 2015 Kingfisher Court the new hospital opened and I was among the selected guests to tour the building. It seemed incredible to me that it had actually happened and that I had played a part in it. I don't think it is perfect but it is a world away from the hospitals where I have been sectioned.

That was an eventful month as Helen headed off to Australia for an unspecified time. I remember her leaving and we went for a walk along the river and saw a family of ducks. The mother duck had her brood safely tucked under her wing and one of mine was about to fly the nest. I burst into tears (which is a rare event; because of medication I don't really laugh or cry).

In the event she stayed 5 months, but it seemed like an eternity to me.

While she was there we flew to Italy (with Inghams) from Cambridge International Airport. I have come to realise that I hate airports more than flying. Cambridge was wonderful small and stress free and we had a really good holiday by Lake Garda. No delays no hassle just great.

Later that year we celebrated our 30th wedding anniversary in Cornwall and had lunch at Rick Stein's flagship restaurant. What I hadn't realised was that Rick Stein owns most of Padstow.

Encountering Tommy – a flatulent Irish horse

Meanwhile Helen, who was in Australia, had, via social media, received a message that her Alma Mater was looking for a French teacher. (She had been teaching French for 3 years at a failing school in Birmingham. Before she took her much needed break to Australia, she had been through 5 Ofsted inspections.) She replied saying she was in Australia but was interested and would get in touch on her return. When she did, it transpired they needed a teacher for French and Spanish, and Helen didn't speak Spanish. So, in March Helen headed out to South America to work with a charity and learn Spanish. She had an amazing time and came back speaking pretty good Spanish with a South American accent! In September she started work at her Alma Mater.

In July that year I went on a Pilates weekend with my lifelong friend Sandra. It was there that I met a counsellor, quite by chance, who would prove very useful to me. She was Australian; her mother had suffered from bipolar and she offered sessions over the phone. I found her a very useful sounding board.

Once Helen was back from South America we had a family holiday in Southern Ireland. We stayed near the Dingle Peninsular and collected a hire car from the airport. We set out on the Sunday morning to explore in the car and found we had a flat tyre. We rang the hire company and they told us we could take it to a local man who would charge 10 euros, or wait for them to come to us which would cost us 100 euros. This seemed very Irish to us but we opted for the local man who was a real character. Among other things we did was visit the Dunloe Gap on a jaunting cart pulled by a very flatulent horse named Tommy. Every now and then we were greeted by clouds of dust as Tommy deposited dung on the road and in between we were blasted by gas from his rear end.

Me with Tommy while he was behaving himself

Later that year we spent a few days in Herefordshire where I learnt that I had forgotten how to ride a bike. I don't know whether any of my medication affects my sense of balance but clearly something had. We hired bikes to go on a cycle trail and I wobbled away from the shop in a very undignified manner. I'm not sure who was more surprised when we returned, the man in the hire shop or me. I was very grateful we were not on the road; as it was I almost fell in a stream.

We returned in time for a family party to mark my aunt's 90th birthday. She is an amazing lady who, until recently, was still swimming once a week and doing aqua aerobics. She could probably still ride a bike too.

Nesting as opposed to empty nesting!

As you may gather, since 2009 life has been fairly humdrum and I have been on a journey of recovery. For someone with bipolar disorder when things are stable there is always a fear they will shift one way or another. So when the year started with us flat hunting with Helen I was a little apprehensive. Moving is always stressful and although it was not my move I would be very closely involved with it. Amazingly the third property we visited was the one, and I was hugely relieved when her offer was accepted. She eventually moved in late May and began to put her stamp on the blank canvas. She made a coffee table out of an old pallet, and some shelves out of wooden wine boxes. She was in her element scouring charity shops for bits and pieces and it was lovely to see her settling down.

In June 2017 we celebrated Nigel's 65th birthday with a family lunch at a Michelin starred restaurant. Jenny was headhunted by South East Water and moved to Tunbridge Wells. She started flat hunting and eventually found a top floor flat in an old mansion, complete with wood burning stove, that ticked all her boxes. She moved in February 2018. It was a huge relief to have them both settled and to have survived all the stress..

Another award?

In between all of this I was contacted, through Richard, the Lead Chaplain, by a member of the clergy and asked if I would speak at a day on mental health. I was very apprehensive but agreed and it went down very well.

Later that year I was nominated for a volunteer award at HPFT by two people. I was thrilled by the nomination made by Richard because I have never been able to describe what a pastoral visitor actually does. He said this:

"Pauline Rhodes has volunteered as a weekly ward visitor on Seward Lodge for upwards of six years. For the past two and a half years, she has also been the spiritual care service's expert by experience.

"In her ward visiting role, Pauline sits for up to an hour and a half at a time with older people, almost all of whom live with the symptoms of advancing dementia, including diminishing verbal skills and cognitive capacity. She is unfailingly gentle, bright and, above all, compassionate with service users. She is willing to enter into their perception of the world, wherever that takes her. For the time that she visits, she is present with whoever she sits.

Even if they cannot recall her visit shortly afterwards, by sitting and being present, she sends out the message that everyone is of value as a human being.

"Pauline also engages with service users' families, who are often visiting when she is volunteering. Her own life experiences enable her to reach out empathically to families and sit with their pain, as they wrestle with the changes in their loved ones that organic conditions inevitably bring.

"Originally a ward volunteer representing the spiritual care service, Pauline now offers her insights as an expert by experience to the chaplains. Her background as a journalist and editor has been invaluable in the service's production of its information leaflets. Her experience of services has challenged the chaplains to see things through the eyes of those to whom they offer spiritual care, not just their own.

"With the spiritual care manager, Pauline is engaged in educating local churches in mental health issues. By telling her own story, she is able to explore with church leaders how they can offer appropriate pastoral and spiritual care to those with chronic experiences of their mental health, challenge stigma and turn round some of the effects of social isolation.

Pauline is a truly committed volunteer and an excellent ambassador for the Trust."

Ready for the award ceremony – very apprehensive

The award ceremony was at the beginning of December and I went along feeling very anxious. My colleague, and fellow volunteer, Jan had also been nominated and we held hands as the award was read out…thankfully we hadn't won. Two middle-aged ladies punched the air in relief. We were at the back and the route to the stage looked a very long way away, but we were delighted that our efforts had been appreciated. Before the refreshments I had to head off to Matlock for the weekend where our family were celebrating my sister's 60th birthday. The weekend was lovely and my family gave me a standing ovation when I arrived at 11.30.

The Beast from the East and another bout of illness

The following January I did another speaking gig at a church in Panshanger in Hertfordshire which was the cause of some anxiety, but it went down well. Unfortunately Nigel developed a pain which kept coming and going and he had to have a series of tests which unnerved me. He is my rock and, although he won't admit it, my carer. The uncertainty about his health affected my mental state. (We would not get a hernia diagnosis for almost a year.)

I was on my exercise machine in our conservatory when the "Beast from the East" arrived. I hate snow and this was driving straight at me. I could almost feel it hitting my face. I became obsessed with it. I was almost paralysed by fear, anxiety and depression. I put the machine away and drew the curtains so I couldn't see the snow but I knew it was still there. I had to keep peeking out at it. I also knew my mental state was fragile and I made an appointment to see my GP and resolved to refer myself for one-to-one cognitive behaviour therapy, which I did. This was February and I finally started in July. In the meantime my GP was excellent; he made me tea and sat and listened to my illogical fears for almost 30 minutes. He later described me as "looking like a hunted animal", and I felt like it. He started seeing me weekly and, although my mental state deteriorated and I didn't want to leave the house, I kept all my appointments with him, partly because Nigel took me.

I became anxious about everything. When I was in the house I was anxious that I should make myself go out and when I was out I was anxious until I was home. It was definitely triggered during the snow, but that had been long gone and I was still suffering. That's the thing about mental illness – it can come on suddenly but it takes what seems like forever to recede. Medication helps, but it takes time...meanwhile Nigel was still experiencing intermittent pain and undergoing tests.

When I say anxiety I don't just mean being a bit worried. I was negative in the extreme. I saw danger everywhere. I shook from head to toe. My mouth went dry and I often had a splitting headache. I felt out of control. I think I am a control freak and so being out of control is really terrifying. I guess I wasn't in control of the weather in February and I needed to somehow manage my fear.
The Fear Fighter's Course (CBT at MiMH) seemed a long time ago and I felt I needed help soon.

Time to quit and time to talk

At the beginning of February I made what was to be my last visit to Seward Lodge. I probably wasn't in a good state but I went in and came to the realisation that all the patients were very ill and mainly unable to communicate. I had always enjoyed making conversation with, or listening to, the patients but I realised that was no longer happening. I felt unnerved by being locked in on the unit and I felt I had hit a wall. I discussed this with Richard, and my colleague Jan, and they both agreed that it was a very different challenge from the one I had accepted at my commissioning in 2010.

Several things had changed. One was that there were fewer mental health beds than there were and more people were being treated in the community. When I first started there was a day hospital, where I made many friends, and two other wards; by the time I left, those that were admitted were more ill, and some were on end of life care. Add to this my fragile mental state, I knew I had made the right decision to quit. However I am not a quitter and I look back on most of my time there very fondly.

When I say I am not a quitter I am aware that determination has got me through a lot. Going back to when I was so very physically ill after I had the girls, one of the nurses said "I'm not quite sure how you've survived – I think it was sheer determination to be there for the girls". Since then most of the time I have been determined to "live alongside" my mental illness and not let it dominate or define me. I always used to pride myself that, as a journalist, I'd never missed a deadline; I still try not to miss things I have in my diary.

A month after leaving Seward Lodge I went to one of the chaplaincy meetings and gave them the two part talk I had given in Panshanger to a group of church leaders and members who wanted to know more about mental illness and how they could help. (I have to say I wasn't very nervous with an audience of three, but the drive over caused me great anxiety. I constantly feared having a panic attack at the wheel.)

This is what I said:

"So what is it like to live with mental illness? Well for me with a diagnosis of reactive bipolar affective disorder, or manic depression as I prefer to call it, it is a bit like being stuck in a glass lift. I can see life but there is an invisible barrier which I cannot overcome. I have no control over whether it will stop on the top floor and I will be manic, or whether it will sink to the basement and I will be depressed. Either way or none it is claustrophobic. Even when I am well I can't cry and neither do I laugh. I exist because of my medication without emotional extremes.

"I hate all mental health labels. Through my illness I have experienced panic attacks, severe anxiety, obsessive compulsive disorder (albeit mildly) and when I have been psychotic I have believed the television and the radio were talking to me. In fact the difference between me when I am manic and when I am depressed is so great that I have often wondered if I have multiple personality disorder. So what's in a name? It's all mental illness which comes about when your brain is playing tricks on you.

"Today I would like to share some of my worst experiences of mental health units and some of my best and then I will try and answer any questions as best I can.

"Almost 25 years ago, I had just lost my father, quite suddenly, and was devastated. Lots of people arrived at my home and I was taken to hospital by two policemen because I was manic and they feared for my safety. I waited a long time, with the police in A&E before I arrived at the psychiatric ward and then I waited, what seemed like forever, to be admitted. During this time, I did myself no favours by trying to escape from the police and activating a fire extinguisher that soaked one of the policemen. (This is the only remotely dangerous thing I have ever done, and I am not proud of it, but if you knew me you would realise that this was totally out of character and the act of a very desperate, manic woman.)

54

"Almost as soon as I was admitted, I was taken to a room and asked to take medication. I refused. In my recollection, before I had even been given a chance to discuss it, I was pinned to the floor by six men. My trousers were torn down and I was injected (with a sedative I presume.) I was still in shock from losing my father; I was terrified by the physical assault and I refused to get into bed. I lay on the floor spread-eagled feeling sick and giddy and convinced (in my psychotic mind) that I had been given a lethal injection. I remember thinking at least I could join my father and I went to sleep on the clinically cold grey floor thinking it was a mortuary slab.

"Sometime later, I went to find a member of staff who simply said "Go back to bed and you will feel better in the morning". I lacked basic clothing and toiletries and I remember thinking the illness had reduced me to a beggar and I felt like the lowest form of animal life.

"I was only in the unit for a little over two weeks although it seemed like months, but during my stay I remember asking to see a Chaplain and have Holy Communion. I recall demanding this once in the middle of the night and being told in no uncertain terms "not to be so stupid". All of my requests were refused and in the end my husband rang the lady Deacon from my church.

"The Deacon was lovely she treated me with gentleness and compassion and it was the most moving and beneficial experience of my stay. I met her in the day room but she was perceptive enough and judged me well enough to say 'you don't want to stay in a day room with the TV and all the smoke, we'll go to your room and we'll make a little altar on your table and light a candle and find peace', and she celebrated the Eucharist with me.

*"In the unit I was in none of the staff **seemed** to know anything about me. No one **seemed** interested in talking to me and what the Deacon offered was a much more holistic approach. She cared for me in a way that I didn't feel the staff did. They were very brusque and dictatorial in my eyes. She was very soft and gentle and motherly and I could respond to that approach much better.*

"Almost ten years later, following the death of my mother, I was sectioned again with mania. This time my admission was much better and the surroundings were much more homely and pleasant. I know I am very sensitive to drugs and I'm always scared to try something new, but again the staff seemed to feel I was refusing my medication and again the crash team arrived to subdue and inject me. This time, to make matters worse, I had a flashback to the last time, which triggered a panic attack, and I felt very claustrophobic and I recall screaming that I would

have the injection if only two people were present, and I did.

"Again in my psychotic mind, the injection would be lethal. I remember saying out loud that my daughters (who were then 14) and my husband could cope without me and I would rather join my parents than live with my illness. Neither of the staff questioned my comments and I was injected and went to sleep, but this time it was on a bed in a pleasantly decorated room.

"During that stay our elderly male Rector came to visit me and, much to his astonishment, I threw myself into his arms saying "Thank God for sanity!" He laughed and said "since when have I been sane? I am a member of the Church of England!" and I felt safe for the first time in many days. "Even when I am very ill, I know I need medication, but I also need a sympathetic ear and the chance to build rapport and trust with someone before I can take drugs and, in my case, when I'm ill, I trust members of the clergy.

"Finally, in total contrast, in 2007 life was manic and I feared I would be sectioned. I went to see my GP, who was brilliant, and he called in my local community team. A lovely female Irish nurse arrived with a young Asian male CPN and they asked me what the problem was. I explained over a cup of tea and we discussed it all very calmly. They and my GP, promised me that I would not be sectioned if I

took my medication, and I did and within a week I had responded and was feeling much better. As my GP wryly observed later: "sometimes you don't need a sledgehammer to crack a nut!"

I followed it by:

"Time is a great healer. On the noticeboard in my office I have a postcard from Rethink which reads 'when your car breaks down you can get help within 60 minutes. When your mind breaks down it can take 18 months.' Even if you get help quicker, time is vital. It takes time to accept you have mental illness and it takes time to learn to live alongside it. It takes time to talk about it and time for others to listen.

"Once a week for six years I volunteered as a ward visitor at an elderly persons mental health unit as part of Richard's spiritual care team, and the only requirement is that you come alongside people and meet them where they are. Sometimes you can spend half an hour in silence just holding a hand but you are giving them time. Time to begin to heal. Other times you can be alongside someone who is manic or psychotic who talks without taking a breath for an hour. You seemingly have no input but you are giving them time to express the chaos in their mind.

"Do I believe I can be cured of mental illness? No, I don't. I believe mental illness is a bit like some

cancers – you can only go into remission. My illness started as manic puerperal psychosis when my twins were born 30 years ago and I have had episodes, as I have said, following the death of each of my parents. In total I have been sectioned five times, and being sectioned is a dehumanising experience. My last episode was 10 years ago and I still struggle with the trauma of being taken to hospital in handcuffs by the police and then being pinned to the ground and injected. Having said I don't believe I can be cured I do believe I have begun healing.

"So how has my church helped me with this? I have been to numerous healing services and received the laying on of hands and have regularly come away disappointed and depressed but on one occasion I was invited to stay for coffee afterwards and I did. It was a small group of mainly elderly people who took me under their wing. There was an elderly gentleman who had been a churchwarden and who was losing his sight and he commented that he liked my perfume and asked me what it was called. This took me by surprise but I told him it was Rive Gauche by Yves St Laurent and I became his 'Rive Gauche lady'. Every week he would ask me to sit with him and tell him what cakes were available and I felt useful and valued. Another elderly lady confessed that she too suffered from manic depression and I became her special friend and we discussed 'flying with God' when we were manic and being totally divorced from Him when we were

depressed. I grew to look forward to Wednesday mornings and the little group who became my mentors. So I realise now the healing began in an unexpected quarter. They were not healing my illness but they were healing me. My self-esteem and self-confidence were at rock bottom but they made me feel valued again. (On the subject of self-esteem, someone with mental illness once described her recovery as taking "baby steps". When a baby learns to walk it often falls over and sits on its bottom and gets up and giggles. When you suffer a bout of mental illness you fall but each time it is harder to get up and laugh.)

"During the time I was going to regular healing services our church was thinking about employing a parish administrator and the Rector asked me if it was something I would consider. He rang me and asked me and said he didn't expect an immediate answer but I felt maybe this was a calling I could follow. So for three and a half years I became the first parish administrator. I had moved from running my own PR company prior to the birth of my twins to taking on the hitherto uncharted territory of parish administrator for a trial period of three months to help out. He had known me since just before my daughters were born, and they were now 12. So we were not exactly strangers, but having said that, when you come to work very closely with someone, you get to know them very much better. He was very confident in my abilities, not least because he was not computer literate and I was, but there were

many times when I would joke that the computer was the work of the devil designed to drive me to distraction. However, for all my mistakes and heartache with the computer, I gradually began to make the job of parish administrator happen.

"I was utterly amazed that so many of my seemingly lost abilities returned. Behind the title of parish administrator I was no longer simply a manic depressive. I functioned in many ways as professionally as I had done before my illness but the job was very different. There were many times when people complimented me on my diplomacy or tact, my thoughtfulness or my kindness, and I began to realise that they were witnessing aspects of my character which had developed through my own experience of illness. I hope I was never hard-hearted and hurtful to people with health issues, but I realised I had become really interested in people, and their illnesses and problems. Although most of my work was working from home on a computer, I really enjoyed the small amount of work I got involved with, especially with the elderly and infirm.

"Throughout this time the Rector and his wife were very supportive there were lots of tears and tissues and cups of tea at the Rectory (not to mention chocolate) and there were many laughs too. It is hard to laugh when you are on your own stuck in a 'glass lift' with manic depression, not knowing whether the lift is going to go up or down. You have no control and it is a very scary place to be but with

someone alongside you it is easier to bear. (This was in the days before my present medication).
"I believe I have learned to live alongside the illness and I encourage others to try and do the same. It is always there but I choose to ignore it as far as possible. I take my medication daily and I try and do regular exercise (although I'm not very good at it). I have learned to put up with the side effects of my medication. I have monthly check ups with my GP and I have a fantastic support group of family and friends.

"Many years ago, long before my illness I remember reading that an opal is only made of sand and silica and it is nothing until it is broken and the light gets in and lets it emit the most beautiful rays. I have an opal in my engagement ring and I often wonder if, as humans, when we have been broken by mental illness, especially manic depression, we get a more beautiful perspective on life...

"So when you are dealing with people with mental illness look for the beauty in the person not for the blackness in the illness. Finally if pastoral work is not your strength, try and build a pastoral care team who can come alongside others and give them valuable time."

These two talks have formed the basis of what I said at the Diocesan Mental Health Day in the following October and the Clergy Training I am still involved in. The Diocesan Mental Health Day drew about 60 delegates and my audience included a Bishop. For someone suffering from anxiety this was a big deal and when it was over I was on a high, which thankfully didn't last long.

Many people have said that I am brave to give these talks, but I believe the bravest thing I've ever done was to get up from the "mortuary slab" and ask for help. Even if I didn't get it immediately.

Breaking new ground

A month later I had a mini school reunion with two former pupils from my year and one teacher. We met over a Chinese meal in Stevenage Old Town and, although, as a mental health patient, I felt like the weakest link I soon realised that there were those from my year who had fared much worse, and I discovered one had been murdered. It was a sobering thought. (I had yet to own the title expert by experience)

Given that I was still struggling with crippling anxiety and fearing panic attacks at every turn, it is remarkable that I agreed to a weekend away in Bath with Nigel in April. It didn't start well. As we crossed a toll bridge with one car's width he hit the gate mechanism and dented the side of my car. Saturday evening saw a tremendous thunderstorm which tested my nerves as well, but we did manage to go to the fashion museum which I loved. Partially because of my anxiety, we left early to come home for a funeral.

Now I knew that Helen had been dating a man since the previous November but we had never met him. I think this was partially because of my mental state. Breaking new ground is hard for me at the best of times and probably makes it hard for others too. A Saturday morning was designated for the meeting. They would come here after parkrun. To cut a long story short, David ended up eating my flapjack for his breakfast. I had not realised they would not have eaten but, true to form, I had made flapjack.

He, very politely, said he'd never had flapjack for breakfast before but he managed two pieces. Hopefully that made a better impression on him than the jittering wreck that was me. It turned out he is an engineer so he and Nigel have much in common.

In July I finally got to see my CBT counsellor and she was very good. I struggled with leaving the house for the appointments but I kept them all and it was very beneficial.

While I had been housebound I had been doing a lot of silk painting and I held another coffee morning where I raised £183 from card sales. Mind in Mid Herts (MiMH) in Hertford were delighted and I felt that some good had come out of my anxiety. I continue to find silk painting therapeutic and I still raise money for MiMH from my card sales.

One Friday in August Helen had asked to come to dinner and I was looking forward to seeing her. I had made Boeuf Bourguignon in the slow cooker and then Nigel had taken over the dinner. This was a bit unusual because normally one or the other of us cooks – we don't generally work in relays. I received a text message from Helen saying she had been delayed but would be with us about 8pm.

I was aware that Nigel was receiving text messages but thought nothing of it. Eventually there was a ring at the door bell and there stood...Helen...or was it Jenny...with a man!

Jenny had decided it was time we met Tom, the man in her life, but didn't want me to get stressed about it. So the whole family had conspired to confuse me and I think I walked round in several circles repeating "I don't believe it!" Heaven knows what Tom thought of me but we are still on speaking terms and when we went to Kent in the September, we met Jenny and Tom for a meal. The original meeting was a lovely surprise but I'm not sure I'm very good at being surprised.

Recovery – the importance of family and friends

Last November saw me meeting "The Professor". She is a mental health specialist that you can be referred to only once and she had agreed to see me. I had a two hour appointment attended by Nigel and my CBT counsellor. We covered my illness from its start to the present day. We discussed medication and its side effects and numerous other issues. Nigel told her that we had got better at managing the illness primarily through early intervention with drugs. I came away feeling mentally battered. It had been a hard two hours and I had come away knowing that Jenny and Helen could inherit it and that it would probably get worse with age. I am sure there were positives, but my mind was not full of them. I had a splitting headache and Nigel took me out to lunch and gave me painkillers. Despite this negativity I began to feel better than I had done for some months and I started planning ahead.

After Christmas I hosted a birthday-cum-Christmas party for Tom, Robin, Jenny, Helen, Greg (Jacqui's boyfriend) and David. They all have birthdays between November 20 and January 1. Jacqui, Nigel and I were the only ones not in "the birthday club". It was lovely to have them altogether and we did a group selfie. I knew then that surrounded by family and friends is how I need to be.

That selfie. Left to right: David, Helen, Tom, Jenny, me, Jacqui, Nigel, Greg and Robin

I want to share my recovery journey with others to give them hope. Being alone with my illness is the worst possible scenario. Friends and family are everything to me. I have a dwindling number of friends from my parents' generation whom I ring for a chat. I try not to mention my illness and I always try and make them laugh. They know me as "Paul" – she is the person I was before my illness and she had a good sense of humour. I still try and emulate her.

I decided to share my recovery by writing a book. The pen may be mightier than the sword but, in my case, it is also mightier than mental illness. I say this as an Expert by Experience.

Postscript:

The difficult we do at once the impossible takes a little longer.

February 2021

Michael Ball, Captain Sir Tom and me...

I had planned to publish this book on Mental Health Awareness Day on October 6 2020 but life had other ideas so to bring it up to date I need to tell you about Michael Ball, Captain Sir Tom and me. To celebrate my 60th birthday and the girls' 30ths I planned a 305th birthday party with them and six friends all with birthdays between November 20 and

Me with my unexpected guest

March 21. It was booked for Saturday February 29th. It was to be a small gathering of just 50 people with cheese and wine and three balloons a 3 0 5 but then Michael Ball gate crashed! Life became surreal. I have to say in his defence that he did not come in person but head first as a life size cardboard cut-out!

This caused much merriment and set a rather different tone to that I expected. Robin, Jacqui and Greg had transported him from London and what a great addition my hero made to the party. That

70

evening I also learnt I was to become a great aunt for the first time; my daughters were to be bridesmaids and a friend who had been wheelchair bound arrived on crutches. It was a momentous occasion and I was on a "high" which was to last until March 23rd just two days after my actual birthday. It was great I photographed Michael on my bed and he took up residence in my lounge by the TV so that I could keep an eye on him.

In my manic mind he would be replaced by the real thing on my birthday but of course life is not like that. My birthday was a Saturday and although I had a lovely day with flowers and chocolates and jewellery, it was a little bit of a come down when Michael didn't arrive.

I am used to going from high to low because of my illness but March 23rd saw me plummet. The prime minister, Boris Johnson, announced total lockdown because of Covid 19.

In my catastrophic thinking we would all die. I could see no future. I folded Michael Ball up and put him behind the sofa. Reality (and worse) had hit with a vengeance. How would we survive if we couldn't buy food? How would I get my medication? What was there to live for? My mind was racing with negativity. I couldn't even see my Dr for a regular check up let alone a crisis…

It just went on and on…a big black pit with no sides to climb up.

My husband was pragmatic. He was planning how we could cope and me phoning the Dr was high on the list. When I finally got through I have no idea what garbled story I told him but he decided that we needed to "tweak" my medication and so together we embarked on a journey of weekly phone calls.

Life from then is a bit of a blur but my overriding fear was of being Sectioned. Six times in 60 years was quite enough. Despite everything, and because of the rock that is my husband, and the exceptional calmness of my GP, things began to fall back into place. Albeit a place neither I nor anyone else had ever been in before.

I tried my hand at crocheting and knitting for the new baby and, much to my amazement, I managed to create two blankets, two cardigans and two hats.

One thing which changed was my inability to go to church which had served as a benchmark in my life. Zoom church was formed but I found it very alienating and strangely although I could see others I felt very divorced from them. I joined a few times but then I gave up and started listening to Michael Ball on Radio 2. There is something about him that seems so genuine and so familiar. He has been with me, as I have said, in his music through some of the worse episodes of my life when I have been

Sectioned and it gives him a special place in my heart and mind.

On April 12 I was listening to his show when he interviewed Captain Tom Moore who was planning on celebrating his 100th birthday by walking 100 laps of his garden. He seemed a lovely gentleman of the same generation as my late father. I was captivated by his story and so was Michael.

By the end of the programme Michael suggested his fundraising could reach £300,000. As we all know his story went worldwide and he raised over 30 million for the NHS but Michael had not finished yet…together they recorded "You'll never walk alone" which went to number one in the charts and made Captain Tom the oldest person ever to be No1. As Captain Tom confessed to Michael, he "had never known the words in the right order and now the whole world does!"

I can't help feeling Michael was also instrumental in him receiving his much-deserved Knighthood which gave us such an endearing image of the Queen with him on her only public appearance during lockdown.

My father always had the maxim that all good things must come to an end and the Captain Sir Tom's story along with the extra publicity Michael helped to generate was no exception.

Just a week ago, Captain Sir Tom Moore passed away. His was an exceptional story and one which helped me, along with many others, through lockdown. For me it also struck a chord when Michael Ball paid tribute to him saying "I needed inspiration. I needed a light at the end of the tunnel and he was it." As he would have said "Tomorrow will be a better day" but then he cheekily confessed to Michael "because it never comes!" Thankfully his legacy will live on in the hearts and minds of those whose lives he touched and the Captain Sir Tom Moore Foundation.

As for me for three months I have had a back problem and in order to keep moving I have been walking round and round our cul de sac. I haven't raised any money for charity but it has given me time to reflect on an extraordinary time in my life. I have settled in to a "new normal". To satisfy my gregarious nature, I WhatsApp a group of friends daily. I make phone calls to elderly members of our congregation who live alone and do my Pilates class on Zoom.

I have enrolled on Slimming World online because during the first Lockdown I put on a half a stone (3kg). This regime includes "Chocolate Time" at 8.15 in the evening! It also involves planning menus and shopping lists. The "new normal" has heralded long lie-ins and getting ready for bed ridiculously early along with staring at four walls in despair for hours on end. It has also produced disturbing dreams/nightmares of losing things and people that are dear to me.

I have been out of my comfort zone twice in a big way. The first was to do a live radio interview for Mental Health Awareness Week and taking part in clergy training on mental health on Zoom!
All of that said, anxiety attacks still grip when I feel I need to go out and then again when I am out and I yearn the safety of home.

The new life has a new routine and I cling to that. I also cling to the hope that "this, too, shall pass" …and this book will finally be published.
As a tribute to all those who have helped me through it all I would like to quote words from Michael Ball and Brian Kennedy:
Just When….

Just when I thought that I couldn't go on
Just when the sun left the sky
Just when I thought that I'd never grow old
You gave me the reason to try

Just when my body felt broken and bruised
Nothing could ease all the pain
Just when my whole world was falling apart
You put me together again

You were the only one
help me to carry on
Help me find hope and desire

All that I want to do is stay in love with you
With all that we've been through
You make me want to try

And deep in my soul I know
You gave me room to grow
Made me let go of the past

You gave me dignity
Showed me the way to be
You believed in me
You gave me wings to fly

Just when the music started to fade
Just when my words wouldn't rhyme

Just when my colours were all turning grey
You changed them and made them shine

Just when I needed the chance to believe
Just when I needed to care
Just when I needed somebody to love
You came and you answered my prayer

Just when I needed somebody to love
You came and you answered my prayer